LECTURE

MEDICAL

LECTURE NOTES ON
MEDICAL VIROLOGY

D. J. JEFFRIES
BSc, MB BS, FRCPath
Division of Virology
Department of Medical Microbiology
St Mary's Hospital Medical School
London

BLACKWELL SCIENTIFIC PUBLICATIONS
OXFORD LONDON EDINBURGH
BOSTON PALO ALTO MELBOURNE

Editorial offices:
Osney Mead, Oxford OX2 0EL
(*Orders*: Tel. 0865-240201)
8 John Street, London WC1N 2ES
23 Ainslie Place, Edinburgh EH3 6AJ
52 Beacon Street, Boston
Massachusetts 02108, USA
667 Lytton Avenue, Palo Alto
California 94301, USA
107 Barry Street, Carlton
Victoria 3053, Australia

First published 1987

Set by Setrite Typesetters Ltd
Hong Kong
Printed and bound
in Great Britain

DISTRIBUTORS

USA
Year Book Medical Publishers
35 East Wacker Drive
Chicago, Illinois 60601
(*Orders*: Tel. 312-726-9733)

Canada
The C. V. Mosby Company
5240 Finch Avenue East
Scarborough, Ontario
(*Orders*: Tel. 416-298-1588)

Australia
Blackwell Scientific Publications
(Australia) Pty Ltd
107 Barry Street
Carlton, Victoria 3053
(*Orders*: Tel. 03-347-0300)

British Library
Cataloguing in Publication Data

Jeffries, D. J.
Lecture Notes on Medical Virology.
1. Virus diseases
I. Title
616.9'25 RC114.5

ISBN 0-632-01703-1

Contents

Preface

Clinical virology has become a most important discipline during the last two decades. Major advances in molecular biology, electron microscopy, immunoassay techniques and cell culture have led to the development of rapid diagnostic methods. Specific antiviral drugs have been developed and, at present, increasing resources are being diverted to attempts to produce vaccines and drugs to counter human retrovirus infections. Hardly a week passes without a significant addition to our knowledge of viral infections. This book is intended to provide a basis for the interpretation of these developments. The chapters are based on a series of lectures given to clinical medical students, over a period of many years, at St Mary's Hospital Medical School, Paddington, London. I have not, however, felt constrained to produce the minimum of information necessary to satisfy the examiners in the MB.BS. Part 4 examination of London University. By producing a more detailed explanation of each topic it is hoped to stimulate and interest medical students, and practitioners, in this exciting area of medicine. It should also provide an introductory text for students in other subjects, particularly biological sciences, medical laboratory science and nursing.

I have resisted the temptation to include photographs of patients with viral infections. To do so would have raised the costs to a level which would have been prohibitive for most students. The reader is directed to the many excellent colour atlases and textbooks of infectious diseases to supplement this text.

I am indebted to Dr Peter Morgan-Capner, Preston Public Health Laboratory, who carefully read each chapter and made many helpful corrections and suggestions. Any remaining errors are mine, not his. I also thank Dr Rodney Rivers, Deputy Director, Paediatric Unit, St Mary's Hospital Medical School, for Fig. 7.1, Margaret Mobberley, E. M. Unit, Queen Charlotte's Hospital for Fig. 6.2 and Dr Stanley Tyms for other photographic material.

D. J. Jeffries

Chapter 1
Nature of Viruses

Viruses are the smallest known infectious agents (20–300 nm diameter). They were originally recognized as filterable infectious agents as they were able to pass through filters that were used to retain bacteria. This phenomenon was first recognized by Iwanowski in 1892 in his studies of tobacco mosaic virus. Viruses infect humans, animals, plants and bacteria and only multiply within susceptible living cells. By definition, therefore, they are obligate intracellular parasites. Most viruses show a high degree of species specificity and require specific receptors to enable them to attach to, and infect, a host cell.

Virus structure

The main components of viruses are nucleic acid and protein. They lack the structural and enzymatic components of bacteria such as cell walls and ribosomes and rely on the host cell to provide many of the facilities for macromolecular synthesis. The major differences between viruses and other infectious agents are illustrated in Table 1.1. Viruses contain one type of nucleic acid, either DNA or RNA, and this is enclosed in a protein shell or capsid. Single virus particles are

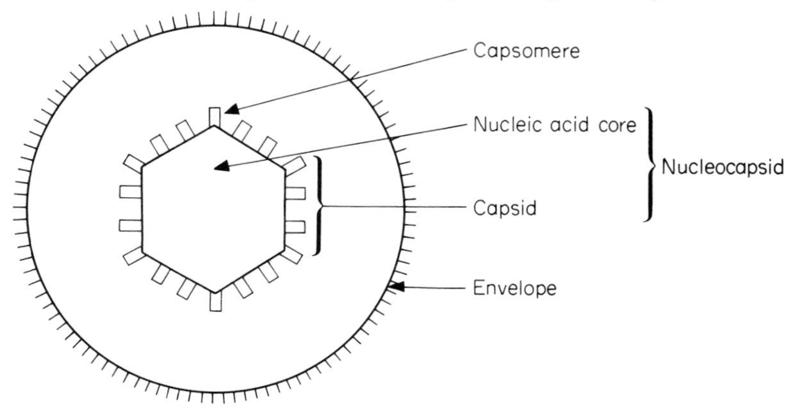

Fig. 1.1 Schematic diagram of virus structure.

Table 1.1 Comparison of viruses and micro-organisms.

Infectious agents	Growth in non-living media	Contains DNA and RNA	Contains ribosomes	Replicates by binary fission	Sensitive to antibiotics	Sensitive to interferon
Bacteria	+	+	+	+	+	—
Mycoplasma	+	+	+	+	+	—
Rickettsia	—	+	+	+	+	—
Chlamydia	—	+	+	+	+	+
Viruses	—	—	—	—	—	+

termed virions and some virions have an outer lipoprotein coat or envelope. The structural components of a typical virion are shown schematically in Fig. 1.1. The type of nucleic acid and its arrangement (double or single-stranded) characterizes a particular virus family and provides a logical basis for classification (see below). The capsid, which encloses the nucleic acid and protects it from degradative enzymes, is composed of one or more types of subunit termed capsomeres. This type of repetitive subunit structure may be achieved with a minimal use of genomic coding capacity and this reflects the simple structure of most viruses in comparison to bacteria. Two types of structure predominate in most virus families; helical and icosahedral symmetry. With helical symmetry (Fig. 1.2) the capsomeres are

Fig. 1.2 Helical symmetry; the capsomeres are arranged along the helical nucleic acid molecule and the entire nucleocapsid is normally enclosed in a membrane.

arranged along a nucleic acid helix and the coiled nucleocapsid is enclosed by a surrounding lipoprotein envelope. An icosahedron has 20 faces (each an equilateral triangle), 12 vertices and 30 edges. Capsomeres, which vary in number depending on the virus family, are arranged in a symmetrical manner on this stable structure. The subunit structure of viruses may be visualized by electron microscopic examination of particles after negative staining with a heavy metal stain such as potassium phosphotungstate. Some of the larger viruses (e.g. poxviridae) have a more complex structure. Viruses (helical or icosahedral) may acquire an envelope during the process of budding through a host cell membrane. With herpes simplex virus the phospholipid envelope forms as the virion buds through the inner nuclear membrane while that of influenza viruses is derived from the cytoplasmic membrane of the infected cell.

Viral envelopes contain glycoproteins and the carbohydrate components often reflect the host cell in which the virus was produced. The glycoproteins are important antigens and, because of their position on the outside of the virions, are frequently involved in neutralization reactions. Some viruses have specific surface structures which are necessary for attachment to permissive cells. These include influenza virus haemagglutinin and the penton fibres of adenoviruses (Fig. 1.3). Although, as already stated, viruses rely largely on the host cell for provision of replicative machinery, some (e.g. herpes simplex) induce or encode host enzymes by the viral genome while others

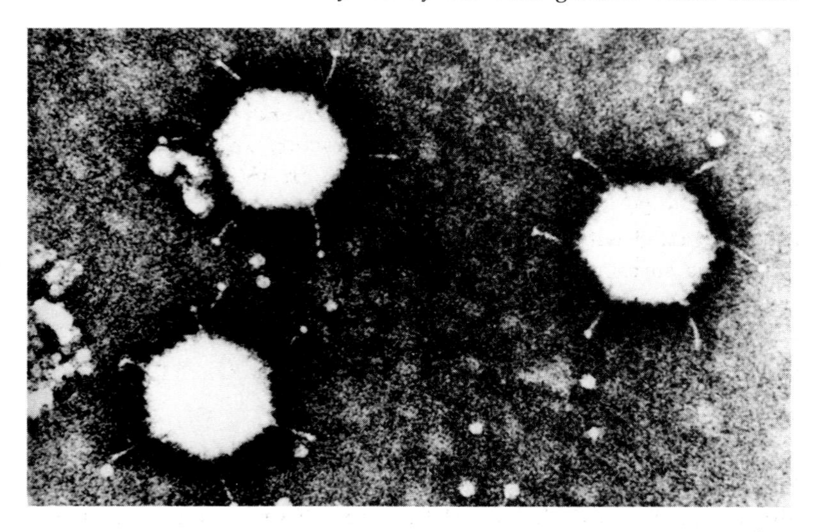

Fig. 1.3 Electron micrograph of adenoviruses showing penton fibres.

contain enzymes that synthesize nucleic acids. Influenza viruses contain an RNA polymerase and the Retroviridae contain RNA-dependent DNA polymerase.

Classification

Viruses may be classified on the basis of biological and physicochemical properties or by the diseases they produce. The latter approach is far from satisfactory as a single virus type may produce many different patterns of disease. Table 1.2 shows the classification of the major virus families based on chemical and physical properties. Within each family viruses are usually allotted to genera on the basis of antigenicity.

DNA viruses

Parvoviruses

Parvoviruses are very small, single-stranded DNA viruses (20 nm) which replicate in the nucleus of the infected cell. While some members can replicate autonomously others, e.g. adeno-associated satellite viruses, are defective and require the presence of an adenovirus or herpes virus to produce infective progeny.

Hepadnaviruses

Three virus types that infect mammals (human, woodchuck and ground squirrel) and one that infects ducks are known. The surface component is overproduced during replication of the viruses in liver cells. This is the hepatitis B surface antigen (HBsAg, Australia antigen) associated with hepatitis B virus infection. The complete virion (42 nm) is surrounded by a lipid-containing envelope and contains DNA which is partially double-stranded. It also contains a DNA-polymerase that repairs the single-stranded region to make fully double-stranded molecules of 3200 base pairs.

Papovaviruses

The name of this family is derived from the papilloma and polyoma viruses together with the vacuolating agent (SV40). They are icosahedral viruses (45–55 nm), containing double-stranded circular DNA,

Table 1.2 Physico-chemical classification of viruses

Nucleic acid	Capsid symmetry	Enveloped or naked	Ether sensitivity	Number of capsomeres	Size of virus particle*	Molecular weight of nucleic acid†	Physical type of nucleic acid‡	Family
DNA	Icosahedral	Naked	Resistant	32	18–26	1.5–2.2	SS	Parvoviridae
				72	45–55	3–5	DS circular	Papovaviridae
				252	70–90	20–30	DS	Adenoviridae
		Enveloped	Sensitive	162	100	90–130	DS	Herpesviridae
	Complex	Complex coats	Resistant		230 × 400	130–240	DS	Poxviridae
					42	1.6	DS circular	Hepadnaviridae
RNA	Icosahedral	Naked	Resistant	32	20–30	2–2.8	SS	Picornaviridae
				?	60–80	12–19	DS segmented	Reoviridae
		Enveloped	Sensitive	32?	30–90	4	SS	Togaviridae
	Unknown or complex	Enveloped	Sensitive		50–300	3–5	SS segmented	Arenaviridae
					80–130	7	SS	Coronaviridae
					c.100	7–10	SS segmented	Retroviridae
	Helical	Enveloped	Sensitive		90–100	6–15	SS segmented	Bunyaviridae
					80–120	5	SS segmented	Orthomyxoviridae
					150–300	5–8	SS	Paramyxoviridae
					70×175	3–4	SS	Rhabdoviridae

* Nanometres (nm). † Molecular weight ($\times 10^6$). ‡SS = Single-stranded; DS = Double-stranded.

with 72 capsomeres. They replicate within the nucleus, produce latent and chronic infections, and have the potential to induce tumour formation.

Adenoviruses

Many different serotypes exist in man (at least 39) and other animals. The virions are naked icosahedra (70–90 nm), containing double-stranded DNA, enclosed in a capsid comprising 252 capsomeres. Some serotypes have the capacity to induce tumours in newborn hamsters but they have not been associated with malignancy in man.

Herpesviruses

The icosahedral nucleocapsid (100 nm) has 162 capsomeres and contains double-stranded DNA. It is surrounded by a lipid-containing envelope which is essential for infectivity and gives the complete virion a diameter of 150–200 nm. Herpesviruses are found in many animal species and five members of the family infect man; herpes simplex types 1 and 2, varicella-zoster virus, cytomegalovirus and Epstein–Barr virus. Herpesviruses have the characteristic of establishing a state of persistent infection, without mature virus production, known as latency.

Poxviruses

Poxviruses have a brick-shaped or ovoid morphology (230 × 400 nm). The DNA is double-stranded and the complex structures are bounded by a lipid-containing membrane. The virions contain several enzymes including a DNA-dependent RNA polymerase and, unusually for DNA viruses, replication takes place entirely within the cytoplasm of infected cells.

RNA viruses

Picornaviruses

This name is derived from pico (small), RNA viruses. They are naked icosahedral viruses (20–30 nm) which are ether-resistant and contain single-stranded RNA. The two main groups which infect the human are the rhinoviruses (>100 serotypes causing common colds) and enteroviruses (poliomyelitis, coxsackie- and echoviruses). Rhinoviruses are acid-labile, have a high density and an optimal growth temperature of 33°C. Enteroviruses are acid-stable, have a lower density and replicate at 37°C.

Reoviruses

Reoviruses are the only RNA viruses known to have double-stranded RNA and this is segmented and enclosed in an ether-resistant icosahedral capsid (60–80 nm). The family includes the original reovirus genus plus the rotaviruses (so called because of the characteristic wheel-shaped arrangement of the capsomeres) and orbiviruses. Members of the orbivirus subgroup are represented in many species including man (Colorado tick fever), animals (blue tongue of cattle and sheep), insects and plants.

Togaviruses

The icosahedral virion is enclosed in a lipid-containing envelope (total diameter 40–70 nm) and it is therefore ether-sensitive. The particles mature, and acquire their envelope, by budding from the host cell membrane. This family includes group A and B arboviruses and rubella virus.

Arenaviruses

The name, arenaviruses, is derived from the Latin word for sand (arena) and denotes the granular appearance of the virions viewed by electron microscopy. The granules are thought to be non-functional ribosomes derived from the cell from which the virion evolved. Arenaviruses are highly pleomorphic (50–300 nm) and the lipid envelope contains segmented single-stranded RNA. The family includes Lassa fever and related viruses and lymphocytic choriomeningitis virus (LCM). Most members have a rodent host in their natural cycle.

Coronaviruses

Coronaviruses are pleomorphic (80–130 nm) with an envelope enclosing an unsegmented single-stranded RNA molecule. The virions are characterized by a striking fringe (or corona) of surface projections known as peplomers. The particles develop in the cytoplasm and mature by budding into cytoplasmic vesicles.

Retroviruses

The single-stranded RNA is of the same polarity as viral messenger RNA and exists as duplicate copies in enveloped particles (90–120 nm). The virions contain a reverse transcriptase (RNA-dependent DNA polymerase) and replication is initiated from a DNA provirus that is integrated within the genome of the infected cells. Three subfamilies of retroviruses are recognized. These are the oncoviruses which induce tumour formation in many animal species, lentiviruses which cause slow virus diseases e.g. maedi and visna in sheep (the AIDS) associated retrovirus has been tentatively assigned to this subfamily) and spumiviruses (apparently non-pathogenic viruses of primates).

Bunyaviruses

This large family of viruses are all transmitted by arthropods (mosquitoes or sandflies). They are enveloped particles (90–120 nm), of helical structure, whose genome is comprised of triple-segmented single-stranded RNA. They replicate intracytoplasmically and bud through the cell membrane. Approximately 70 members are antigenically related to Bunyamwera virus and another 50 are unrelated but morphologically similar.

Orthomyxoviruses

All orthomyxoviruses are influenza viruses that infect humans and animals. The particles are 80–120 nm in diameter although they can produce filamentous forms. The helical nucleocapsid is enclosed in an envelope which usually possesses surface projections (haemagglutinin and neuraminidase). The single-stranded RNA is comprised of eight segments. During replication the nucleocapsid is assembled in the nucleus and the haemagglutinin and neuraminidase accumulate in the cytoplasm. The virions mature by budding through the cell membrane.

Paramyxoviruses

Paramyxoviruses are similar to, but larger than, the orthomyxoviruses. The virion (150–300 nm) contains a helical nucleocapsid with a width of 18 nm (6–9 nm for orthomyxoviruses) and the molecular weight is four times greater. Replication and assembly of virions occurs totally in the cytoplasm.

Rhabdoviruses

These helical particles show some tendency to form a bullet-shape (70 × 175 nm). The envelope has 10 nm spikes, the genome is single-stranded and particles bud from the cell membrane. This family, which includes rabies virus, is represented in many animal and plant species.

Filoviruses

Marburg and Ebola disease viruses have been included in this new family. The virions have a uniform diameter (80 nm) and vary in length (up to 1500 nm). Some particles are branching, others are circular or in other forms. The helical nucleocapsid contains one molecule of single-stranded RNA surrounded by a lipid-containing envelope with surface projections.

Replication

Viruses establish a variety of different relationships with living cells. Some induce a rapid shutdown of cellular metabolism and redirect cellular metabolic systems to synthesize viral components. Others establish a symbiotic relationship which allows continuing production of progeny virus with little or no disruption of cellular function. Some viruses can establish a state of latency, in which their nucleic acid is maintained in a non-productive state. Viruses gain entry to cells by attachment to receptors on the cell surface which are recognized by specific proteins in the viral coat. This process, termed adsorption, is followed by uncoating which results in the release of the nucleic acid into the cytoplasm. Uncoating often occurs by fusion of the viral and cell membranes, or engulfment of the whole virion by the cell membrane, followed by enzymic disruption of the protein coat.

RNA viruses

Viral nucleic acid is transcribed to messenger RNA (mRNA) which can then express the viral genetic information. This process is accomplished in different ways depending on the type of virus. Orthomyxoviruses contain RNA polymerases that transcribe the single-stranded viral RNA (negative strand) to mRNA (positive strand). This mechanism operates with all negative strand RNA viruses (e.g. orthomyxoviruses, paramyxoviruses, rhabdoviruses). Picornaviruses and togaviruses are positive strand viruses and the viral RNA serves as its own mRNA. On entering the host cell the viral RNA is translated to produce RNA polymerase and also inhibitors of host cell synthetic processes. The RNA polymerase synthesizes replicative intermediates, first a partially double-stranded RNA and then a complete double strand consisting of positive and negative RNA. Viral RNA in the form of single positive strands is then synthesized and these strands are translated into viral structural proteins which are assembled around the viral RNA to produce complete virions. All these events occur in the cytoplasm and the progeny virus is released by lysis of the host cell.

DNA viruses

With the exception of poxviruses, all DNA viruses replicate in the nucleus. After entry into the cell, and enzymic removal of the protein coat, the viral DNA is released into the nucleus. One or both strands of the DNA are transcribed into specific mRNA which in turn is translated to synthesize the early viral products, such as DNA synthetic enzymes, which are necessary for continuing replication. The effect of these early viral gene products on cell metabolism is variable; herpes simplex viruses induce a rapid shutdown of cell metabolism while other viruses (e.g. cytomegalovirus) stimulate host cell DNA synthesis. As the viral DNA continues to be transcribed late viral functions become apparent. Messenger RNA migrates to the cytoplasm and is translated to synthesize capsid proteins. These structural components are transported to the nucleus to be assembled around the newly formed viral DNA to produce new viral particles. The progeny virus is then released, either by disruption of the cell, or by budding from the cell membrane. A viral envelope may be acquired during the process of budding either from the cell membrane or, as with herpes simplex viruses, from the nuclear membrane.

Transformation

Some DNA and RNA viruses have the capacity to induce tumour formation (oncogenic viruses) and can produce the phenomenon of cellular transformation. Transformed cells have particular properties that distinguish them from normal cells. They have lost the capacity for their growth to be inhibited by proximity of other cells (contact inhibition) and acquire the ability to grow in semi-solid media with a requirement for less serum than normal cells. They can be grown continuously in culture and do not show the ageing phenomena exhibited by normal cells. DNA tumour viruses replicate in cells of their natural hosts but rarely, if ever, produce tumours in them. Although unable to replicate in heterologous hosts they may induce transformation. Vacuolating agent (SV40) replicates without transformation in monkey kidney cells but may transform rodent cells in which it is unable to produce infectious virus by integrating genes into the host cell genome. The viral genome contains regions that code for early and late events. The late region codes for viral coat proteins that are not produced in transformed cells. The early region codes for early proteins, such as the SV40 tumour antigen, that are necessary for the replication of viral DNA in permissive cells and for transformation. The transforming protein must be continuously synthesized to allow maintenance of the transformed state. Other viruses (e.g. papillomaviruses) do not integrate with the host cell genome but their DNA persists in a free state in an extrachromosomal site or episome.

RNA tumour viruses are members of the retrovirus family and produce a particle associated reverse transcriptase. This enzyme produces a DNA copy of the viral genome and this is integrated into the nucleic acid of the infected cell. After integration some cells produce progeny virus as a result of expression of the integrated provirus with RNA and protein synthesis. Other cells retain an unexpressed provirus which replicates with the host chromosomes as though they were cellular genes. Expression of these endogenous retroviral genes may occur but they are normally controlled by other, host cell, genes. Cellular DNA sequences homologous to proviral DNA from retroviruses (cellular oncogenes) have been identified in the chromosomes of many animal species. Their function is largely unknown, but evidence of their differentially enhanced expression in the fetus suggests that they may have a physiological role in intra-uterine development. Disturbance of expression of a cellular oncogene, either by insertion of a retroviral provirus at an adjacent site or by soluble activating factors are thought to be ways in which retroviruses can induce tumour formation. In addition some animal retroviruses can promote acute tumour formation by inserting a viral oncogene, a potent transforming sequence carried within the viral genome, into the host chromosomes.

Further reading

Fields B. N. and Knipe D. M. (1986) *Fundamental Virology*. Raven Press, New York.

Matthews R. E. F. (1982) Classification and nomenclature of viruses. *Intervirology*, **17**, 1–199.

Smith K. M. and Ritchie D. A. (1980) *Introduction to Virology*. Chapman and Hall, London.

Chapter 2
Infection and Dissemination

In the previous chapter emphasis was placed on the dependence of viruses on living cells. Although viruses can survive for varying times in the environment their continued existence rests on their ability to invade, replicate within, and be disseminated from the host organism. The process of infection with a virus must be distinguished from disease. Most human viruses produce a spectrum of disease processes and many infections are subclinical or asymptomatic. As a single virus, e.g. hepatitis B, can cause acute hepatic failure and rapid death in one individual and a totally asymptomatic infection in another there is clearly a major host component in determining the disease pattern of many virus infections.

Portals of entry

Most of the body is covered with skin and because this possesses a protective layer of dead cells it presents an effective barrier to most viruses. Where the skin surface is discontinuous and living cells are exposed to the environment there is a greater opportunity for viruses to adhere and establish an infection. Most viruses, therefore, enter the body through cells in the respiratory, gastrointestinal and urogenital tracts or by conjunctival infection.

Skin

Some viruses have adapted to a life-cycle which is dependent on biting arthropods. Mosquitoes, sandflies, ticks and mites feed on human blood and during the process of penetrating the skin may deposit a virus into the subcutaneous tissues or directly into a capillary. Myxoma virus is transmitted to rabbits by contamination of the mouth parts of mosquitoes and fleas (mechanical transmission) while other viruses, e.g. yellow fever, multiply within the insect vector. Hepatitis B virus and, on rare occasions, human immunodeficiency virus (HIV), can be transmitted by puncture of the skin by contaminated sharp instruments and needles. Rabies virus is transmitted from one infected animal to another by a bite and the altered behaviour pattern resulting from encephalitis in the animal increases the likelihood of a bite occurring and hence facilitates the survival of the virus. When viewed microscopically an apparently intact skin surface often harbours minute cuts and abrasions. These may occasionally provide a portal of entry for papillomavirus and herpes simplex virus with the development of warts and herpetic whitlows.

Respiratory tract

The respiratory tract offers a very large area of moist, living cells which are potentially exposed to any viruses that may be present in the inspired air. In the alveolae the barrier between the air and the circulatory system is only one cell thick. Not surprisingly, therefore, highly efficient local defence mechanisms exist to counter the continuous threat of infection. Mucus is produced by goblet cells in the ciliated epithelium of the nose and lower respiratory tract and also by subepithelial mucus glands. Foreign particles including viruses are trapped by the mucus and carried by ciliary action to the back of the throat and removed by swallowing. This process has been described as the mucociliary escalator and is extremely efficient at preventing foreign material from entering the alveolae. It becomes less efficient if the ciliary system is damaged and cigarette smoking has been shown to inhibit ciliary action. Viruses which possess a haemagglutinin (e.g. influenza) can evade the action of mucus by attaching firmly to respiratory epithelial cells. This explains why influenza can be highly transmissible in a non-immune population. Very small particles (<5 μm) can pass directly into the alveolae. Alveolar macrophages provide a further very important defence mechanism and, under normal circumstances, the particles are phagocytosed and destroyed.

Gastrointestinal tract

Many viruses produce symptoms and signs in the pharynx and adjacent areas. The exact route of entry is usually unknown and they are often described as ororespiratory infections. The herpesviruses, cytomegalovirus and Epstein–Barr virus occasionally produce glandular fever, a prominent feature of which is often a severe sore throat. These have been described as kissing diseases as it is assumed that they are only likely to be transmitted by intimate oral contact probably involving transfer of infected cells. The continuous movement of the gastrointestinal tract together with production of mucus which lines the mucosa probably affords protection against viral attachment. In addition the presence of concentrated acid in the stomach followed by proteolytic and lipolytic enzymes in the duodenum means that only the most resistant viruses are likely to enter the small intestine in a viable state. Picornaviruses illustrate this point. Enteroviruses are acid stable and can enter and replicate in the intestines while rhinoviruses which are acid labile are restricted to the upper respiratory tract.

Urogenital tract

The mucous membranes of the male and female genitalia are an important potential portal of entry for certain viruses and other sexually transmitted infections. Herpes simplex viruses and papillomaviruses are examples of local infections that are commonly transferred by this route and the genital tract may provide access for blood-borne viruses of which hepatitis B and HIV are most significant. Although the terminal urethra may occasionally be infected by herpes simplex it is rare for viruses to establish infection in other areas of the lower urinary tract. The frequent cleansing action of urine may explain this.

Conjunctiva

The conjunctivae are protected by tears and the cleansing action of the lids. Conjunctivitis, corneal ulceration and scarring can result from transfer of herpes simplex viruses from other sites into the eye. The nasolacrimal duct offers a possible route of infection from the eye to the upper respiratory tract. Hand to eye contact is a frequent event and this may be an important mechanism for transmission of respiratory viruses.

Note that another important portal of entry for viruses is the placenta. Infections of the fetus are discussed in Chapter 15.

Dissemination of infection

Local infections

Many viruses enter cells on mucous membranes and remain localized to the epithelium. Disease normally develops within a few days of infection, there is little or no invasion of underlying tissues, and the virus is shed directly to the exterior. Influenza viruses, rhinoviruses and, in the gastrointestinal tract, rotaviruses are viruses of this type.

Systemic spread

If a virus has the capacity to invade subepithelial tissues it may enter the lymphatic system. If it is rapidly inactivated by macrophages in the marginal sinuses of lymph nodes the immune response is initiated and, although there may be regional lymphadenopathy, the infection does not progress. If the virus is not inactivated, and particularly if it can survive or replicate in macrophages or lymphocytes, the particles will pass through the lymph nodes and enter the bloodstream. The virus is likely to be distributed to distant parts of the body and establish infection in the reticuloendothelial system. This blood-borne dissemination from the initial replication site is termed the primary viraemia and it is an asymptomatic event occurring during the incubation period. Following a period of replication in distant sites such as the liver and spleen large amounts of progeny virus may be released into the bloodstream. This normally heralds the onset of clinical effects in a systemic viral infection and further sites of infection in other organs may follow. If virus lodges in skin capillaries a rash may be a prominent feature. Measles, smallpox and chickenpox are examples of this type of systemic virus infection.

The nature of viraemia depends on the virus. Some viruses, e.g. poliomyelitis and yellow fever, are carried free in the plasma. Viruses carried in monocytes (e.g. smallpox) or lymphocytes (e.g. Epstein–Barr virus and measles) are protected from antibodies and other factors in plasma and can be disseminated widely by these cells. The virus of Colorado tick fever infects erythrocytes in the bone marrow and enters the circulation from this site.

Persistent infections

Many viruses produce acute disease, which may be local or generalized, and they are then eliminated completely by host defences. Others persist in the body for periods of months, years or in some cases the life of the host. A persistent infection in which there is continuous virus production is termed a chronic infection; this is the situation in the infectious carrier state (HBeAg positive) of hepatitis B. Viruses which can survive for long periods in a non-productive form with the potential for reactivation are said to exhibit the phenomenon of latency. Herpesviruses establish lifelong latent infections. A collection of persistent virus infections of the nervous system have been termed slow viruses and these are discussed in Chapter 12. This term, which is far from satisfactory, is applied to infections which have a very long incubation period followed by a disease process which is usually subacute but invariably fatal.

The ability of a virus to persist in the host and shed infectious particles either intermittently or continually facilitates transmission and survival of the agent. Studies of infection in small isolated communities illustrates this point. Measles, which produces acute disease with lifelong immunity, does not normally establish a persistent infection. A population of at least 500 000 is necessary to provide enough susceptibles to allow the infection to remain in a community. Chickenpox (varicella-zoster virus) establishes a latent infection which may re-emerge many years later as shingles. This ensures that the virus remains in a potentially infectious state within the community and a population as small as 1000 is adequate to allow continuing infections.

Mechanisms of persistence

Immunosuppression

The elimination of viruses is normally achieved by specific immune mechanisms. If these are impaired, particularly those involved in cell-mediated immunity, a virus infection is likely to become chronic. Active immunosuppression by chemotherapeutic agents, which is used to produce tolerance to organ grafts, is likely to result in reactivation and continuous shedding of previously latent herpes viruses. Similar effects are seen in patients with immunodepressive disease states, particularly malignancies, and in the acquired immune deficiency syndrome (AIDS) in which the cellular immune system is profoundly disturbed by infection with HIV.

Ineffective antibody

There are a number of persistent virus infections in which the host fails to produce antibody which has the ability to neutralize the virus. The failure to respond rapidly to the infection or to produce significant levels of neutralizing antibody may be the main reason for their persistence. Attachment of non-neutralizing antibody to viral particles may obscure but not inactivate sites which are critical for infectivity and these blocking antibodies may facilitate prolongation of the infection. The retroviral disease of sheep, visna, induces a sluggish humoral antibody response which takes up to two years to reach its peak. Human immunodeficiency virus (HIV) stimulates high titres of antibodies which have poor neutralizing capacity.

Privileged sites

Some viruses are able to persist by establishing infection in tissues that are inaccessible to the full power of the immune system. This isolation may be assisted by the binding of non-neutralizing antibody to infected cells thus preventing recognition and elimination by cellular immunity. Infection of epidermal cells with wart viruses only proceeds to active replication when the infected cell is keratinized and out of contact with the immune system. Rubella virus has been shown to have persisted in lens tissue removed at operation from patients with a known history of congenital rubella and in whom the virus became undetectable in other sites many years before.

Antigenic change

Two members of the Retroviridae are known to undergo antigenic change during the course of infection within the host. Visna virus produces mutations in the envelope gene which result in antigenic change in envelope glycoprotein. This means that the antibody produced early in the infection has less neutralizing activity against later variants and this may be of importance in maintaining viraemia. The retrovirus of horses, equine infectious anaemia virus, also shows similar variation in the envelope gene region. Disease occurs in a relapsing pattern and each episode is produced by the emergence of a new antigenic variant. A burst of virus production stimulates the immune response and the illness, an anaemic crisis, results from antibodies reacting with viral antigens bound to erythrocytes leading to their lysis. The immune responses then control the infection and the horse returns to normal health until the next attack.

Persistence of viral nucleic acid

Viruses which can exist within the host in the form of integrated or episomal nucleic acid will not be recognized or attacked by the immune system until they become active and produce antigens. Retroviruses use the viral enzyme reverse transcriptase to produce a complementary DNA copy of their RNA genome which is then incorporated in the genome of the infected cell. This integrated sequence or provirus may remain unexpressed as a latent infection or it may lead to viral protein production and trigger an immune response. Herpes simplex viruses are known to persist in a latent state in cranial and spinal ganglia and, although the balance of evidence is in favour of retention of viral DNA rather than a low level steady state infection, the exact form and location of the nucleic acid is unknown. Epstein–Barr virus is known to persist in B lymphocytes mainly in episomal form but the virus also integrates with the cell genome.

Growth in the immune system

A number of persistent viral infections are known to involve cells of the immune system and particularly antigen presenting cells. It seems logical to assume that if a virus can invade and replicate within this system it is likely to be difficult or impossible to eliminate. HIV, which is known to infect T4 lymphocytes and antigen presenting cells, produces persistent and probably lifelong infection. In mice, lymphocytic choriomeningitis virus and lactic dehydrogenase virus, both of which infect macrophages, produce lifelong persistent infections. Invasion of the immune system is not, however, inevitably followed by viral persistence; measles virus which replicates in T lymphocytes is normally eliminated from the body. It is possible that those viruses which can achieve a state of persistence in the immune system can manipulate immune responses to maintain this existence.

Non-immunogenicity

A group of transmissible agents which cause subacute degeneration of the nervous system, although of unknown nature, have been grouped together with other agents producing similar effects and termed slow viruses. These agents, which include scrapie, kuru and Creutzfeldt–Jakob syndrome, induce spongiform encephalopathy and have the characteristic of being totally non-immunogenic. This means that following infection the agents can replicate and, in the process, produce their clinical effects without apparent recognition or intervention by the immune system. These agents are discussed more fully in Chapter 12.

Further reading

Mahy B. J. W., Minson A. C. and Darby G. K. (1982) *Virus Persistence*. 33rd Symposium Soc. Gen. Microbiol. Cambridge University Press, Cambridge.
Mims C. A. and White D. O. (1984) *Viral Pathogenesis and Immunology*. Blackwell Scientific Publications, Oxford.

Chapter 3
Immune Responses

Viral infections are controlled by a very complex system of non-specific and specific immune responses. Studies of individuals with specific immune defects indicate that different viruses are countered by different aspects of the immune system. Variations in host responses suggest that the immune response to a single virus may vary both qualitatively and quantitatively in different individuals. Most information concerning immune mechanisms comes from studies of isolated phenomena which may have no relationship to occurrences *in vivo*. If a single defect is present in an individual its full impact may be masked by compensation by other sections of the immune response. This flexibility of host defences appears to provide a fail-safe mechanism in the event of congenital or acquired abnormalities.

Macrophages

Macrophages phagocytose viruses and are important cells in controlling virus infections. They are present in many parts of the body and those in the alveoli of the lung and sinusoids of the liver (Kupffer cells) are of critical importance in preventing entry of organisms from the respiratory tract and gut. Macrophages offer a non-specific scavenging system which usually results in inactivation of viral particles. Some viruses can, however, replicate within them and this may lead to dissemination of the infection. If macrophages are supporting the growth of a non-cytocidal virus a chronic, often asymptomatic infection may result. If the virus is highly destructive the host may be overwhelmed by widespread aggressive disease. The importance of macrophages in determining the outcome of viral infections is seen by comparing virulent and avirulent strains of closely related viruses. The virulent and avirulent strains of ectromelia virus (mouse pox) can be distinguished by their behaviour in cultured macrophages. Virulent strains can establish productive infection while avirulent strains are unable to replicate. In mice the virulent strains produce a fatal infection by establishing infection in liver macrophages and this leads to destruction of liver tissue. The avirulent strains are unable to replicate to the same extent in the liver and the infection is easily controlled.

Newborn mice are particularly likely to develop generalized infection and death with herpes simplex viruses when infected intradermally. They can be protected by transfusion of macrophages from adult animals. Adult mice develop a similar susceptibility to viraemic spread of herpes simplex if their macrophage function has been blocked by infusion of silica or colloidal carbon. The newborn human, particularly if premature, is also prone to suffer from uncontrolled dissemination of herpes simplex viruses. This vulnerability subsides several days after birth at the time of maturation of the macrophage system.

Macrophages and related cells are central to the development of specific immune responses by presentation of antigens to T cells and B cells. Over 50 soluble products (monokines) are secreted by macrophages of which interleukin 1, which serves as an essential signal for T cell maturation response to antigen, and alpha interferon are likely to be important in virus infections. If macrophages become armed with antibody they can specifically attach to, and kill, virus infected cells. This is a form of antibody dependent cell-mediated cytotoxicity (ADCC).

Polymorphonuclear leucocytes

There is little evidence that polymorphonuclear leucocytes (PMNs) are involved directly in controlling viral infections but they are important components of acute inflammatory responses. As in other circumstances where tissues suffer damage PMNs provide a significant contribution as scavengers of dead cells and other debris. Although PMNs do not play a major role in controlling viral infections some viruses have been shown to infect them and disturb their function. The reduction of bactericidal capability of PMNs which have previously been infected with influenza A viruses may be of importance in the pathogenesis of post-influenzal staphylococcal pneumonia.

Natural killer cells (NK cells)

NK cells are non-specific leucocytes which are capable of killing virus infected cells and tumour cells. They are stimulated by alpha interferon and viral glycoprotein and their activity is markedly increased within 48 hours of viral infection. Little is known about their origins or their precise role in the early control of an invading virus.

Killer cells (K cells)

The armed macrophage, previously mentioned, is one example of a cell which is capable of ADCC and is termed a K cell. At least two other types of leucocyte (non T−non B lymphocytes and PMNs) can destroy virus infected cells provided virus specific IgG is present. The effector cells are non-specific and attain their specificity by binding to receptors on the Fc section of the immunoglobulin. This phenomenon of bridging target cells and effector cells with antibody is independent of complement activation and has been shown, *in vitro*, to provide a very efficient system for lysing infected cells. As with NK cells the relative importance of this system for controlling viral infections *in vivo* has not been clearly defined.

Interferons

Interferons are a diverse group of biologically active proteins (broadly grouped as alpha, beta and gamma) that are produced early in viral infection and have a wide spectrum of activity against many viruses. More than a dozen different interferon genes have been identified and cloned by recombinant DNA technology and their amino acid sequences have been elucidated. Most have molecular weights within the range 16 000−23 000 atomic mass units and the three main types are antigenically distinct. Alpha and beta interferons are produced in response to viral infection and virtually any type of cell in any vertebrate species tested has shown the ability to respond to viral infection in this way. Gamma interferon is only produced by lymphocytes after antigen-specific or non-specific (mitogen) stimulation and is classed as a lymphokine which has immunoregulatory activity. Although beta and gamma interferons show some degree of species specificity interferons stimulated by one virus are active against many other types of viruses (DNA and RNA).

Antiviral action

Interferons bind to cell surface receptors and this leads to a cascade of at least three different enzymes. These are 2′−5′adenylate synthetase, endoribonuclease and a protein kinase. The 2′−5′adenylate synthetase and the protein kinase are activated by the presence of double-stranded RNA and this is therefore assumed to be present in the replication cycle of both DNA and RNA viruses. The 2′–5′adenylate synthetase catalyses the production from ATP of an unusual series of oligonucleotides known as (2′–5′)pppA(pA)n and these activate the endoribonuclease to destroy mRNA in virus infected cells. This process is one of a number of biochemical activities attributed to interferons and their exact modes of action and importance in antiviral activity in nature remain unsolved.

Immunomodulation

It is clear from many studies that interferons have many potential effects on the control of the immune system. The fact that some of these actions appear to be conflicting probably indicates that their effects are dose dependent and determined by strict temporal relationships. The known effects of interferons on immunocompetent cells are summarized in Table 3.1.

Table 3.1 Biological effects of interferons

Inhibition of virus multiplication
Inhibition of cell division
Changes in plasma membrane
Increase in histocompatibility antigens
Increase in β microglobulin
Increase in Fe receptors
Increase in negative charge
Increase in lectin binding
Reduction in release of murine leukaemia virus
Reduction in cell motility
Disturbance in organization of microfilaments and fibronectin
Immunomodulation
Macrophage—activated
NK cell—maturation, recycling and cytotoxicity increased
T cell—proliferation suppressed, lymphokine release enhanced
Ts cell—activated
Td cell—decreased or increased activity
Tc cell—increased cytotoxicity

Other effects of interferons

Many other actions of interferons have been described and some of these may be of importance in viral infections. All three types have been shown to have an inhibitory action on mitosis in normal and malignant cells. The relative potency of the individual types varies depending on the cells concerned. This effect may be important in certain prolonged viral infections particularly in the fetus and may be the main reason for the low birth weight and developmental delay seen in congenital rubella. With the increasing availability of cloned interferons this effect is being exploited in attempts to treat malignancies. Interferons have a number of effects on cell membranes and these include increases in lectin binding, expression of histocompatibility antigens, beta 2-microglobulin and Fc receptors, and decreases in cell motility and budding of murine leukaemia virus from infected cells.

Complement

The complement pathway involves the sequential activation of at least 20 proteins and functions by mediating and amplifying immune and inflammatory reactions. The classical pathway is triggered by antigen-antibody combination and has a number of antiviral effects. Recruitment of complement may assist in the neutralization of viral particles, that have been coated by immunoglobulins, by providing additional masking of viral proteins necessary for infectivity. In the case of enveloped viruses the presence of the lytic complement components may facilitate lysis of the virus and release of the nucleic acid. Complement may assist in the lysis of infected, antigen-bearing cells and, by enhancing the inflammatory response in tissues, the introduction of immunocompetent cells may be important in the local control of virus growth. Some viruses including measles, mumps, herpes simplex and parainfluenza can activate the alternative complement pathway and neutralization can occur in the absence of specific antibody. This may be an important early defence mechanism because it will be available immediately after viral invasion and before the appearance of specific immunity.

Cell mediated immunity

Cell mediated immunity (CMI) is of major importance in eliminating many viruses from the body and recovery from disease. Viral infections of tissues are normally accompanied by infiltration with lymphocytes and macrophages and the importance of CMI can be demonstrated by animal experimentation and study of humans with defects in their immune systems. In animals, depletion of T cells by removal or destruction of the thymus or by treating with antilymphocyte serum results in increased susceptibility to a number of viral infections including herpes simplex, cytomegalovirus and coxsackie viruses. CMI deficiency in humans, whether due to congenital defects such as thymic aplasia or acquired abnormality such as malignancy, AIDS or administration of immunosuppressive drugs, renders the individual more vulnerable to severe infection with vaccinia virus, measles and the herpes viruses. In addition to this, as described in the previous chapter, these infections are more likely to persist.

T lymphocytes mature from stem cells under the influence of the thymus gland. Different functional populations have been distinguished and these may be identified by monoclonal antibodies to surface antigens. Cytotoxic T cells (Tc) recognize viral antigens on cell surfaces only in association with glycoproteins encoded by the HLA,B or C complex. As antigens are present on infected cells before virus production is complete, direct destruction by Tc cells offers a potentially important mechanism for eliminating viral infections.

Delayed-type hypersensitivity is mediated by another population of T cells (Td). Viral antigens on the macrophage surface, in association with D/DR antigens, are recognized by Td cells and this results in lymphokine release (including gamma interferon) and migration of macrophages to the site. Helper T cells (Th) also respond to antigen-bearing macrophages and, following activation by interleukin 1,

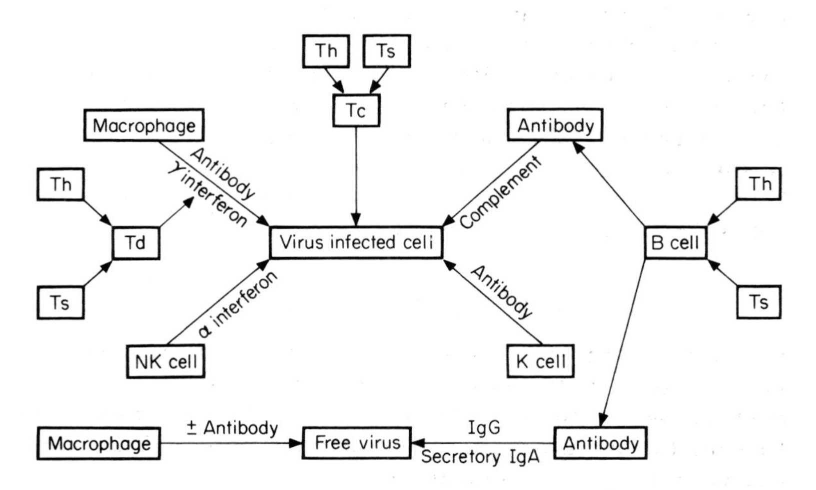

Fig. 3.1 Diagram to illustrate the interrelationships between the major components of the immune response.

secrete several lymphokines called 'helper factors'. These factors trigger clones of B lymphocytes (antibody producing cells) and also, probably through interleukin 2 (T cell growth factor), stimulate Tc and Td cells. Suppressor T cells (Ts) regulate the immune response by inhibiting Th, Tc and Td cells after they have performed their functions. Obviously this mechanism, which is little understood at present, is likely to be complex and intricate and it is possible that some viruses may be able to interfere with this aspect of CMI in order to achieve a state of persistence. The interrelationships of the different cells involved in the CMI response to viral infections are illustrated schematically in Fig. 3.1.

Antibody

B lymphocytes, which are derived from multipotential stem cells in the bone marrow (or liver in the fetus), respond to neo-antigens by division and differentiation into antibody-secreting plasma cells. This process is controlled by antigen-specific and non-specific factors produced by Th cells. In addition to the generation of antibody producing cells, clonal expansion of B lymphocytes leads to the production of memory cells. On re-exposure to the antigen these memory cells respond rapidly with the production of high titres of specific antibody (mainly IgG). An unexplained feature of humoral immunity is the persistence of circulating antibodies to viruses encountered years before, despite the lack of further exposure to those specific antigens. It has been suggested that this is achieved by persistence of viral antigens, possibly on the surface of follicular dendritic cells. The spleen and lymph nodes are the major sites of synthesis of IgM and IgG antibodies directed against antigens in the blood and lymphatics. Lymphoid tissue in the submucosal tissue of the alimentary and respiratory tracts (e.g. adenoids, tonsils, Peyer's patches) produces IgA antibody directed against antigens in epithelial cells. In the context of immunization against viruses, more IgA is stimulated by oral or respiratory administration than by using a percutaneous route. Some IgA circulates in the blood and is secreted in body fluids such as milk and saliva. IgA is present on mucosal surfaces as a dimer. This is formed by linking of two molecules of the monomeric form by a J chain and 'secretory piece' as they pass through the epithelial cells. Serum IgA is mainly in the monomeric form. The presence of IgA in mucus offers an important local defence against virus invasion. The duration of protection is short lived, however, and this partly explains the frequency of respiratory tract infections and the reason why infection with some viruses (e.g. respiratory syncytial virus) can occur repeatedly throughout life. Repeated exposure to multiple antigens has the value of stimulating mucosal IgA and individuals living in isolated communities have been shown to have lower IgA levels and be more prone to severe respiratory infections than those living in cities.

IgM is polymeric and, because of its large size, is confined to the blood system. It is produced early in the course of infection and as the immune response develops it is replaced by IgG. The early appearance of IgM, with its multiple antigen combining sites is probably a major factor in limiting the spread of many viruses. If IgM antibody persists in the circulation it often indicates a continuation of viral replication and establishment of a persistent infection. IgG is the only immunoglobulin which is able to cross the placenta. Therefore the presence of specific antiviral antibodies of the IgM class in the neonate indicates intra-uterine infection with that agent.

Function of antibody

Antibodies are of particular importance in the control of infections that have a significant plasma viraemia such as yellow fever virus and enteroviruses. Hypogammaglobulinaemia does not compromise an individual against most viral infections but the incidence of viraemia and subsequent paralysis following live poliomyelitis vaccine is estimated to be 10 000 times higher in individuals lacking immunoglobulins than in those with normal levels.

A number of actions of antibody can be demonstrated *in vitro* against virus particles and against virus infected cells. As previously emphasized the precise role of each of these mechanisms *in vivo* awaits definition.

Virus neutralization

Certain epitopes on the surface of capsids or viral envelopes are essential for infectivity and, if these critical sites are blocked by antibody, the virus is neutralized. Not all antibodies to surface antigens produce neutralization, however, and the critical sites may be obscured by non-neutralizing antibody. This may lead to dissemination of circulating immune complexes that carry potentially infectious particles. The effectiveness of neutralizing antibody can be seen in the response to rubella infection (Chapter 15). The first antibody to appear is haemagglutination-inhibiting antibody (HAI). This blocks the action of rubella haemagglutinin which is essential for infectivity and the rapid increase in titre of HAI antibody coincides with elimination of infectious virus from circulation.

The exact mechanism of neutralization remains unclear and several workers have shown that it is not simply a process of preventing adsorption. Indeed in some instances viruses have been shown to enter cells but their subsequent replication has been inhibited by pretreatment with antibody. Neutralization may be enhanced by recruitment of complement and it is possible that rheumatoid factor (an anti-immunoglobulin usually of the IgM class) that appears late in many viral infections may also increase the action of antibody.

Opsonization

Combination of viral particles with antibody facilitates their uptake and subsequent killing by phagocytic cells. Agglutination of virions also reduces the number of effective infectious units.

Antibody mediated cytolysis

Antibody attached to cell surface antigens will recruit complement and this may lead to lysis of the cell. The phenomenon is dependent on the presence of foreign antigens and not necessarily complete virus particles and may be important in preventing dissemination of progeny virus from intracellular sites. In addition to this, antibody can act as the critical link between effector cells (killer cells) and target cells in ADCC (see above).

Antigenic modulation

Antibody can alter the configuration of antigens on cell surfaces. This has been demonstrated with measles virus infected cells and may have a role in limiting spread of infection. Antibody combines with envelope antigen and the complex is drawn together or 'capped' and then either shed from the cell or internalized. This leads to interference with virus assembly and particles accumulate within the cell. When the fusion protein is removed in this way from measles infected cells cell–to–cell fusion is inhibited and this may limit dissemination. There may be adverse sequelae to this process as the removal of antigenic recognition may allow the virus to establish a persistent infection and this is thought to be a possible cause of the slow virus disease subacute sclerosing panencephalitis (Chapter 12).

Further reading

Mims C. A. and White D. O. (1984) *Viral Pathogenesis and Immunology*. Blackwell Scientific Publications, Oxford.

Nahmias A. J. and O'Reilly R. J. (1982) Immunology of human infection. Part 2, Viruses. In: *Comprehensive Immunology*, Vol 9. Plenum Press, New York.

Roitt I. M. (1980) *Essential Immunology*. 4th edition. Blackwell Scientific Publications, Oxford.

Chapter 4
Disease Mechanisms

It could be argued that, provided a virus can achieve a satisfactory means of transmission to a new host, it is not in its interests to damage or kill the host. Many viruses produce asymptomatic infections in all or a proportion of those infected and in many cases, as will be illustrated later, disease is caused by the host response and not by a direct effect of the virus. The effects of damage by a virus vary depending on the site of the infection. Destruction of tissue in a skeletal muscle is likely to be tolerated much more easily than a similar process in the brain which is so vulnerable to increases in pressure. Similarly a small area of inflammation on the bowel wall is unlikely to have the same consequences as a lesion on the retina.

Prodromal illness

This is the name given to the non-specific symptoms which herald the onset of disease at the end of the incubation period in a number of viral infections. Hepatitis B is an example of a virus that produces a prodrome. It usually presents with a fever, malaise, myalgia and gastrointestinal symptoms such as abdominal pain, anorexia and bowel disturbance for several days before jaundice becomes detectable. The cause of this illness is unknown and it has in the past been assumed to result from either release of pyrogens from damaged cells or possibly from circulating complexes of viral antigens and early antibody. Early studies on the effects of highly purified alpha and gamma interferons prepared by recombinant DNA technology revealed a surprising toxicity. When injected into normal individuals they regularly produced malaise, myalgia and fever and the similarity of these symptoms to those of acute influenza raises the possibility that the illness experienced in influenza may be mainly the result of endogenous interferon production. The prodromal illness of systemic viral infections, which occurs at the time of maximal viraemia, may also be interferon induced.

Cellular damage

In Chapter 1, reference was made to the effects of virus replication on host cell metabolism. Many viruses including herpes simplex, poxviruses and picornaviruses induce an irreversible shutdown of cellular macromolecular synthesis and this leads to cell death. Although some viral proteins (e.g. adenovirus) have been shown to be toxic to living cells when applied in high concentrations *in vitro*, there is no evidence that toxin production is associated with viral diseases. The histological appearance of cells infected with cytocidal viruses depends on the stage of infection. Early effects are due to changes in membrane permeability and produce cloudy swelling and the cell-rounding seen in cell cultures. As replication continues, inclusions may be seen within the cytoplasm or nucleus depending on the virus concerned. These inclusions which take up histological stains are of two types. One type, e.g. that produced by papovavirus, is composed of aggregates of viral capsids, the other consists of viral components that lack a defined morphology, e.g. the Cowdrey type A inclusions seen in herpes simplex virus infection. The inclusions seen in the cytoplasm of cortical neurons in the hippocampus and other areas of the brain in rabies (Negri bodies) are composed of viral proteins . The appearances of several types of inclusion body are shown schematically in Fig. 4.1.

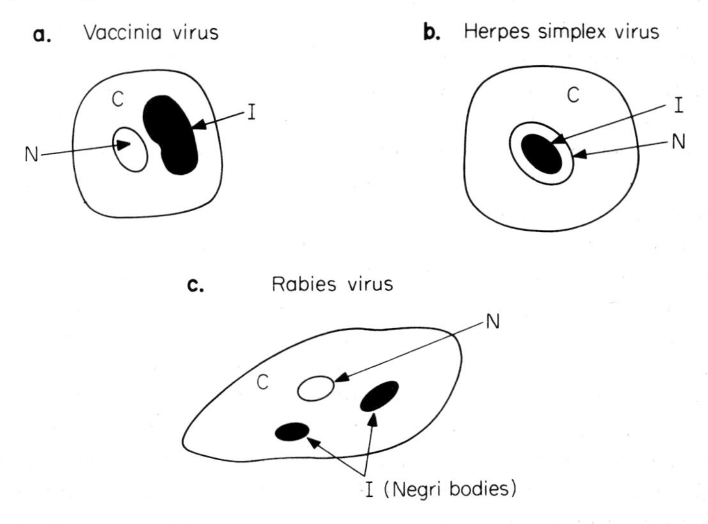

Fig. 4.1 Diagram to illustrate the appearance and location of inclusion bodies. N = nucleus; C = cytoplasm; I = inclusions.

Some viruses are able to induce cell fusion and this leads to the formation of a giant cell or syncytium. Paramyxoviruses and herpesviruses can induce this type of cytopathology (illustrated in Fig. 4.2) and the resulting multinucleated cell is unable to undergo normal cell division and will ultimately be killed by the virus. The mechanisms by which viruses may induce tumour formation in cells are discussed in Chapter 19.

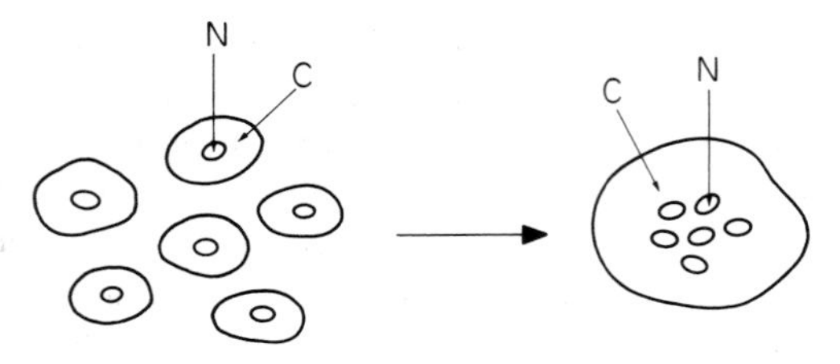

Fig. 4.2 Diagram to illustrate syncytium or giant cell formation. N = nucleus; C = cytoplasm.

Many viruses grow non-cytocidally and bud from the plasma membrane while leaving the cell's macromolecular synthetic processes undisturbed. The continuous production of foreign antigens may, however lead to the formation of circulating immune complexes which may eventually deposit in blood vessels and cause disease in distant sites. Glomerulonephritis which develops in mice infected with lymphocytic choriomeningitis virus is an example of this type of immunopathology.

Organ damage

It is not possible to predict the behaviour of a virus in the intact host from a knowledge of its behaviour in cell culture. Some viruses (e.g. ECHO viruses) are highly cytocidal *in vitro* but frequently produce asymptomatic infections in man. Several common human pathogens (e.g. rotavirus, parvovirus, papillomaviruses) have not been successfully propogated in culture. There are also some interesting and unexplained paradoxes concerning the particular tissue and organ tropisms of certain viruses. Human cytomegalovirus grows most readily in cultured fetal fibroblasts and yet, *in vivo*, it commonly infects glandular tissue and epithelioid cells. Poliomyelitis viruses, although widely distributed within the nervous system of those with the major illness, characteristically destroy the anterior horn cells.

While the rash of herpes zoster can be adequately explained by the escape of virions from nerve endings along a dermatome, no satisfactory explanation has been offered for the centripetal rash of varicella or the centrifugal distribution of variola.

The importance of the site of replication in producing disease has already been emphasized. It is possible, with a number of human viruses to draw analogies between the process *in vivo* and the focal cytopathic effect seen in cell cultures. The lytic foci of herpes simplex virus growing in the temporal lobe of the brain and rubella virus in the fetal lens are examples of local destruction by cell-to-cell spread.

Although there is little evidence for toxin production during viral infections, damage may result from mechanisms other than direct cytocidal infection. A soluble antimitotic factor has been isolated from rubella virus infected cultures and production of a similar substance in the rubella infected fetus could account for the reduced cell mass and underdevelopment of certain organs. One candidate for such a growth regulating substance is interferon which can be produced during early intra-uterine life. Other viruses can exert critical effects on biochemical processes without evidence of widespread destruction. Rabies virus causes its lethal effects by interfering with acetylcholine and other membrane receptor functions.

Immunopathology

The immune mechanisms available for control and elimination of viruses from the body were described in Chapter 3. The presence of viral antigens, which are recognized as foreign material, elicits the expression of immune responses and, in the process, inflammatory reactions, lymph node swelling and cell destruction are likely to ensue. These reactions may be sufficiently pronounced to damage or even kill the host. This type of disease is termed immunopathology. Many manifestations of human viral diseases can be explained in this way. This is also a major reason why a single serotype of a virus may produce a varied spectrum of disease manifestations in an infected population. Thus with mumps virus one individual may have exquisitely painful parotid glands due to acute inflammation and lymph node swelling while another may have a silent infection within the glands. Similarly, hepatitis B virus may be totally asymptomatic in one person, produce classical jaundice in a second and acute hepatic failure in a third.

Hypersensitivity

Hypersensitivity reactions to foreign antigens have been conveniently classified by Coombs and Gell into four main types. There is no evidence that type 1 (anaphylactic) or type 2 (cytolytic) reactions are features of human viral infections.

Type 3 hypersensitivity

Type 3 responses involve immune complex formation and this phenomenon was noted above in the context of persistent non-cytocidal infections. Combination of antigen and antibody leads to complement recruitment and inflammatory responses result. The presence of fixed complexes in tissues or deposition of circulating complexes in small blood vessels can, therefore, lead to organ damage. Circulating immune complexes are commonly formed during the acute stage of viral infections. At this time only small amounts of antibody are produced and its combination with large amounts of viral antigen present in circulation produces soluble complexes that circulate in the vascular system. As antibody production increases, antibody excess complexes are produced and these are opsonized by phagocytic cells. This, in parallel with other immune mechanisms, normally leads to elimination of the virus.

Long term production of soluble complexes with delayed disease due to chronic inflammation may result from the production of poor quality antibody or antibody that is virus specific but non-neutralizing. As described below, immune complexes depositing in skin blood vessels may lead to rash formation. If there is extensive immune complex formation at the acute stage of virus infections, disseminated intravascular coagulation may result. This is an occasional complication of yellow fever and other haemorrhagic fevers and is precipitated by activation of the enzymes of the coagulation system which leads to histamine release and increased vascular permeability. Multiple infarcts due to fibrin deposition occur and consumption of platelets in the complexes together with reduction in prothrombin, fibrinogen and other factors leads to haemorrhage.

Type 4 hypersensitivity

As described in Chapter 3 this type of hypersensitivity reaction is produced by CMI reactions and specifically by Td cells. The classical model of CMI mediated immunopathology is lymphocytic choriomeningitis (LCM) virus infection in mice. LCM given intracerebrally in adult mice establishes a non-destructive meningeal infection. After a period of 7–10 days the mice die from severe meningitis and cerebral oedema. The pathogenesis of this illness is attributed to the development of sensitized T cells because the disease can be prevented by immunosuppressive drugs antilymphocyte serum or neonatal thymectomy. Newborn mice do not react in the same way to LCM and a persistent infection with high levels of virus in blood and tissues is established. Administration of sensitized T lymphocytes from adult animals precipitates the fatal immunopathological reaction. Lung damage from influenza viruses in mice has been related to CMI responses and transfusion of Td cells has been shown to enhance severity.

In humans it has been frequently observed that immunosuppressive drugs, which produce their major effect on CMI, are likely to modify the effects of hepatitis B virus. In consequence, asymptomatic or mild illnesses are common although long term carriage of the virus is frequent. With hepatitis B it appears that in many cases the penalty for elimination of the virus is the immunopathologically induced jaundice.

Although the absence of a competent CMI system renders an individual highly vulnerable to measles virus, and severe pneumonia and gastroenteritis are likely, the classical rash may not develop. This is the pattern of disease seen in malnourished children, who are known to have CMI defects, and it indicates that the classical measles rash is immunopathological in nature and dependent on competent T cell function.

Viral rashes

Rashes or exanthema are common presenting features of viral infections and in some diseases the nature and/or distribution of the rash may be diagnostic.

Vesicles

Several viruses produce vesicular eruptions and in the diseases caused by poxviruses, herpes simplex viruses and varicella-zoster virus the pathogenesis is reasonably well explained. Virus reaches the epidermis either directly through skin abrasions (cowpox, orf, traumatic herpes simplex), via nerve fibres (herpes simplex, herpes zoster) or through the circulation (varicella, variola, herpes simplex) and a cytolytic infection is established. As described in Chapter 9, cell destruction leads to the development of a blister or vesicle. The vesicles in herpes virus infections are superficial and thin walled while poxvirus lesions enter the dermis and scarring results. This process occurs at the acute stage of the infection, before the immune response has developed, and can therefore be attributed to direct viral damage.

Erythema

Erythema is reddening of the skin that is usually due to the increased vascularity accompanying acute inflammation. Its presence can be confirmed by the fact that it blanches on pressure. Prodromal rashes occasionally seen in a number of viral infections including hepatitis B are often erythematous and probably result from immune complex deposition in the skin. Erythema multiforme presents with typical target lesions that may be accompanied by arthralgia, malaise and fever. It usually develops as a drug reaction or as a sequel to infection with *Mycoplasma pneumoniae* or herpes simplex. Some people suffer this reaction with each recurrence of their latent herpes simplex infection. It appears to be an allergic reaction to herpes antigens that is probably immune complex mediated. Stevens–Johnson syndrome is a severe form of erythema multiforme in which the skin is extensively involved and this leads to desquamation. In addition there is ulceration of the oral and genital mucous membranes and conjunctivitis. If the vascular involvement is more extensive erythema nodosum may result in which tender erythematous nodules are present containing antigen, antibody and complement in vessel walls. When small arteries are the site of deposition of immune complexes as may occur in hepatitis B infection, periarteritis nodosa may result.

Maculo-papular rashes

Macules are flat lesions within the skin that cannot be discerned by touch. Papules are raised from the skin surface and are palpable. Two common viral diseases present with rashes which are described as maculo-papular; rubella and measles. The rash of rubella is classically faint and purplish in colour and often comes and goes during a period of approximately four days at the acute stage of the illness. The onset of the eruption coincides with the appearance of HAI antibody, the decrease in viraemia and the development of circulating immune complexes (see Fig. 4.3). In measles the rash also develops at the time of HAI antibody formation and immune complexes may be involved but as stated earlier the rash only forms in the presence of competent T lymphocytes.

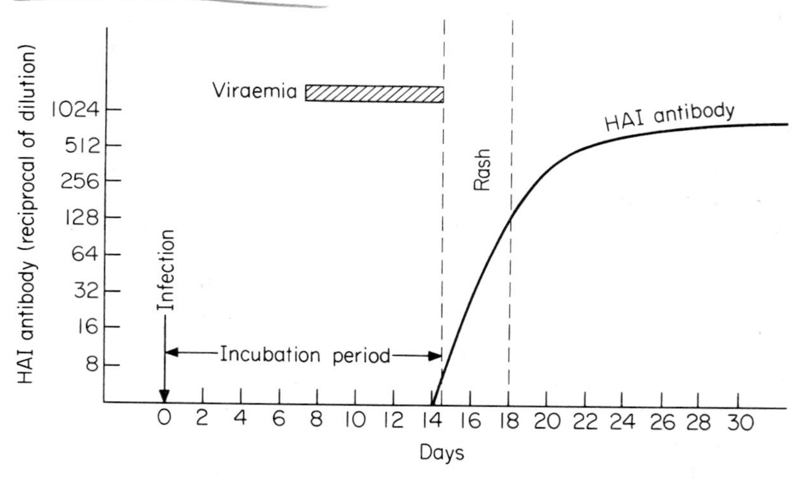

Fig. 4.3 Typical sequence of viraemia, antibody development and rash formation in rubella.

Purpura

Purpuric rashes are the result of haemorrhage into the skin and the presence of large areas of purpura or tiny lesions (petechiae) is confirmed by applying pressure to the skin: in contrast to erythematous lesions the staining of purpura is not abolished by pressure. Purpura may result from direct damage to blood vessels and the rickettsial disease known as Rocky Mountain spotted fever (*Rickettsia rickettsii*) is an example of this. In addition to this any infection that disturbs haemostasis may lead to purpura and often bleeding in other sites. The occasional complication of platelet and clotting factor depletion caused by disseminated intravascular coagulation has already been mentioned and acute hepatic failure due to yellow fever or hepatitis B may also lead to purpura by the reduction in prothrombin levels.

Thrombocytopenic purpura may result from a failure to produce (or release) platelets from megakaryocytes or, as indicated above, consumption of circulating platelets. In congenital rubella the virus affects the haemopoietic system and purpura present at birth is due to low production of platelets. Rubella (and rubella vaccination) in children and adults is invariably followed by a drop in platelet counts although it rarely reaches the low levels necessary to precipitate purpura or other haemorrhages. The mechanism involved is combination of circulating rubella agglutinin with specific HAI antibody and then attachment of platelets to the platelet receptor on the Fc portion of the immunoglobulin. The complexes are removed from circulation by phagocytes at a rate that is faster than the rate of release of new platelets.

Further reading

Mims C. A. (1982) *The Pathogenesis of Infectious Disease.* 2nd edition. Academic Press, New York.

Mims C. A. and White D. O. (1984) *Viral Pathogenesis and Immunology.* Blackwell Scientific Publications, Oxford.

Chapter 5
Prevention and Treatment

Immunoprophylaxis

Viral diseases can be prevented by active and passive immunization. Active immunization, using vaccines, confers long term protection. Passive immunization, with immunoglobulin or convalescent plasma, is short lived.

Viral vaccines

Vaccines may be broadly classified as live or killed.

Live vaccines are prepared by inducing a reduction in virulence in a strain which has been isolated from an infected individual. This process, called attenuation, is usually achieved by passaging the agent in cell culture and other host systems *in vitro*. Less virulent forms are generated by an empirical process of mutation and vaccines are prepared from variants that have acceptably low disease-forming potential while retaining satisfactory immunogenicity. Satisfactory attenuation is demonstrated in laboratory animals before evaluation in clinical trials. It may be possible to influence the production of mutants by applying certain conditions to the culture systems. An example of this is the generation of temperature sensitive (ts) mutants which have a limited range of growth temperatures.

Killed vaccines are prepared from wild virus by inactivation using processes which retain antigenic potential. The traditional inactivation process relied on formaldehyde treatment but more recently β-propiolactone and ethylenimines have been used. Recent developments in virus purification and molecular biology have led to the introduction of subunit vaccines.

There are advantages and disadvantages with both types of vaccine and much effort is devoted to increasing potency and reducing toxicity.

Live vaccines

The main advantage of live vaccines is potency. By infecting the recipient with a less virulent form of the natural virus the immune system is stimulated over a prolonged period by antigens produced in a similar pattern to those of the wild strain. The aim of this approach is to induce a subclinical infection that confers lasting immunity which is similar to natural infection. It also offers the possibility, as with oral polio vaccine, of immunization by a natural route of infection.

The main problems associated with live vaccines are related to safety. If a vaccine is insufficiently attenuated it will cause disease in the vaccinee. Genetic instability may lead to a reversion to the virulence of its ancestor. This is likely to occur if the vaccine virus is transmitted directly from one individual to another. It is this process which accounts for most cases of paralytic poliomyelitis in the western world in which the causative viruses retain the identity of vaccine strains. This serious complication occurs with a frequency of less than once in a million immunizations. To lessen the risks of accidental infection from a vaccinated child it is recommended that the parents receive concurrent vaccination.

Another potential hazard of live vaccines may reside in the cells of the culture systems. Viruses present in the animal from which the cells were obtained may be harboured in a latent or inapparent state. These contaminants may be amplified by culture and then carried into the vaccine stocks. This was a particular problem when monkey cell cultures were used for polio vaccine production and many people have received the monkey virus SV40, a member of the Papovaviridae, as a contaminant. Fortunately, no ill effects have been attributed to this.

Another disadvantage of live vaccines is the interference phenomenon. A vaccine may be inhibited by the presence of another virus either present as a natural infection or if a mixture of live vaccines is administered. This effect which is probably related, at least in part, to interferon production may be overcome by repeating the immunization at a later date. This is the reason for giving three doses of oral polio vaccine (containing three serotypes) to infants. Surprisingly, it has not been a problem with a currently available combined measles, mumps and rubella vaccine. Live vaccines have presented major handling problems in countries with high ambient temperatures and limited facilities for refrigeration. Failure to maintain a cold-chain to ensure the continued viability of thermolabile vaccines has led to unsuccessful immunization programmes in tropical countries.

Recent advances in molecular biology have allowed the construction of novel recombinant viral vaccines. The first of these to be assessed incorporated the gene for hepatitis B surface antigen (HBsAg) in live vaccinia virus. By vaccinating the recipient in the classical method used for smallpox prophylaxis it may be possible to give parallel protection against hepatitis B. This technique has considerable potential and is being applied to other viruses. Clinical assessment is currently being delayed due to anxiety over possible pathogenicity of the vaccinia vector and safer carrier viruses are being sought.

Killed vaccines

Many of the problems associated with live vaccines are eliminated by efficient inactivation processes. The major disadvantage of killed vaccines is lack of potency and this means that resulting immunity is less likely to be long lasting. It is usual to give 2–3 primary injections followed by repeated boosters. It is not possible to use a natural route for administration and the antigens cannot be presented to immunocompetent cells in the same sequence as in natural infection. Inactivated polio (Salk) vaccine, which has been used most succesfully in several countries, has a disadvantage compared to oral (Sabin) vaccine in its need to be given by injection. There have been recent successes in purifying the essential immunogenic proteins of viruses. This has resulted in potent vaccines from which unnecessary antigens have been removed. The hypersensitivity reactions to influenza vaccines have been reduced by splitting the envelope with lipid solvents and purifying the haemagglutinin and neuraminidase subunits. Developments in recombinant DNA technology should lead to production of synthetic subunit vaccines. Thermostability is an important advantage of inactivated vaccines but the need to inject a large amount of material means that they are expensive to produce. Killed vaccines may be safely used in the immunocompromised. This is an important advantage as live, attenuated vaccines are generally contraindicated in this situation.

The viral vaccines in common use are listed in Table 5.1. Details of individual vaccines are given in the sections on specific viruses.

Passive immunoprophylaxis

Immunoglobulin of two types is available to protect against virus

Table 5.1 Viral vaccines in common use

Disease	Vaccine strain	Cell substrate	Attenuation	Inactivation	Route
Rabies	Pasteur	Human embryo fibroblasts	—	β propiolactone (or tributyl phosphate)	IM, or ID
Yellow fever	17D	Chick embryo	+	—	SC
Poliomyelitis	Sabin 1, 2, 3	Human embryo fibroblasts	+	—	oral
Measles	Schwarz	Chick embryo fibroblasts	+	—	SC
Rubella	RA27/3	Human embryo fibroblasts	+	—	SC
	Cendehill	Rabbit kidney	+	—	SC
Mumps	Jeryl Lynn	Chick embryo fibroblasts	+	—	SC
Influenza	A/H3N2, B, (A/HINI)	Chick embryo	—	β propiolactone (or formalin) or haemagglutinin/ neuraminidase subunits	IM
Hepatitis B	Subunit vaccine prepared from donor plasma			Formalin	IM

Table 5.2 Passive immunoprophylaxis

Immunoglobulin	Virus	Considered for use in
Human normal immunoglobulin (HNIG)	Hepatitis A	Contacts of cases, non-immune travellers to endemic areas.
	Measles	Contacts with immunocompromise, debility, malnutrition or chronic lung disease.
Hepatitis B immunoglobulin (HBIG)	Hepatitis B	Health care personnel after inoculation injury, skin or mucous membrane exposure. Protection of newborn of carrier mothers.
Zoster immune globulin (ZIG)	Varicella-zoster	Immunocompromised.
Rabies immunoglobulin	Rabies	Individuals bitten by suspected rabid animal—injected around wound and IM.
Anti-mumps immunoglobulin (supplies limited)	Mumps	Contacts with immunocompromise, debility, pancreatic disease, testicular deficiency and neonates exposed to infection in the mother.

infections. Human normal immunoglobulin (HNIG) is extracted from random blood donors while a range of specific immunoglobulin preparations are obtained from individuals with high antibody levels to particular viruses. Animal sera have been used in the past as a source of antibody but these carry the serious risk of sensitization and induction of anaphylactic reactions. Immunoglobulin preparations are purified by the Cohn fractionation process using cold ethanol. This eliminates the risk of contamination of the preparations with viruses present in the donors.

The average half-life of IgG is 21 days and, although the duration of protection conferred by immunoglobulin depends on the dose given, it is effective for weeks rather than months. Due to the risks of inducing a shock syndrome from aggregated IgG immunoglobulin preparations must, in the absence of indications to the contrary, be given by deep intramuscular injection. In post-exposure prophylaxis the sooner the immunoglobulin is administered after contact the higher is the likelihood of preventing infection. If it is delayed this may not be achieved although attenuation of the illness with consequent active immunization from the natural infection may occur. The main uses of immunoglobulin are listed in Table 5.2 and details are included under specific virus infections.

Antiviral chemotherapy

A small number of antiviral drugs are in routine use and others are in the process of development. The dependence of viruses on living cells for their replication has caused considerable difficulty in devising therapeutic agents that will inhibit a virus without damaging normal cells. Some of the earlier drugs used to treat herpesvirus infections were originally cytotoxics which were found to have some preferential effect on virus infected cells. In some clinical situations antiviral compounds may be considered for prophylaxis but their main use is in the control of acute diseases. Before starting treatment it is important to weigh the likely outcome of the infection against the chemotherapeutic index, and therefore risk of toxicity, of the drug to be used. As in many acute viral diseases the peak of virus replication has passed by the time the disease has fully developed, the sooner specific therapy is commenced the greater is the likelihood of influencing the pathogenesis. If virus persists however, as it may in the immunocompromised, drugs may be life-saving in preventing further dissemination.

Amantadine

Amantadine, l-adamantanamine hydrochloride, (Fig. 5.1) is a symmetrical C10 tricyclic amine. It has been shown to be effective in the prevention and treatment of disease caused by influenza type A virus (subtypes H1 N1, H2 N2 and H3 N3). Its precise mode of action has not been established but it appears to interfere with virus uncoating after penetration of the host cell. Prophylactic efficacy has been reported in healthy adults and children, the chronically sick and the elderly. Infection can be totally prevented in approximately 50% but the majority (70–100%) are protected from the disease. Although

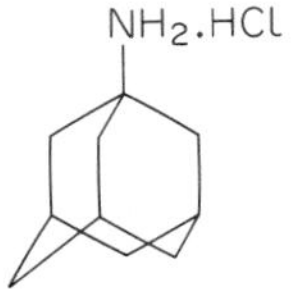

Fig. 5.1 Amantadine.

early studies indicated central nervous system side effects, which limited its usefulness, recent evaluation with a lower dose produced a similar level of protection with no obvious toxicity. Amantadine offers a reasonable alternative to immunization (the success in preventing the disease is similar). In view of the time taken to identify, characterize and prepare vaccines against new serotypes of influenza A virus, this drug may be most important if the world is faced with a virulent pandemic. Oral amantadine is effective in the treatment of acute influenza A provided the drug is given within 48 hours of the onset of symptoms. Clinical trials have shown a reduction in symptom duration and fever of 1–2 days. There have been no controlled studies in influenzal pneumonia and although those patients who have received the drug showed no significant benefit treatment was usually begun late in the illness.

Acyclovir

Acyclovir, acycloguanosine, (Fig. 5.2) represents a major breakthrough in antiviral drug development as it combines potency with a high level of selectivity in its mode of action. Its activity depends on intracellular conversion of acyclovir to its triphosphate derivative. The first stage in this process is initiated by a specific virally coded thymidine kinase (TK) produced by certain herpesviruses (herpes

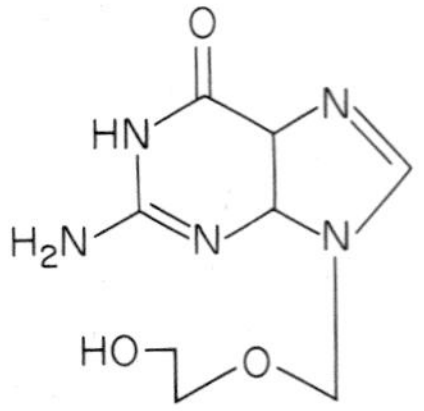

Fig. 5.2 Acyclovir.

simplex 1 and 2, varicella-zoster and herpesvirus simiae). Acyclovir binds several hundred-fold greater to viral TK than to the equivalent cellular enzyme and its phosphorylation is more than a million times faster. Consequently, little or no acyclovir monophosphate is produced in cells not infected by herpes viruses and this accounts for the extremely high chemotherapeutic index. The monophosphate is converted to the di-and triphosphates by cellular enzymes and acyclovir triphosphate is a potent inhibitor of herpesvirus DNA polymerase. This mechanism of action is illustrated in Fig. 5.3. Thymidine kinase deficient mutants of herpes simplex viruses can be readily generated in cell cultures but, although several apparently resistant strains have been reported in immunocompromised patients, drug resistance has not been a widespread problem.

Acyclovir is remarkably non-toxic and is given prophylactically to immunocompromised patients (particularly transplant recipients) who

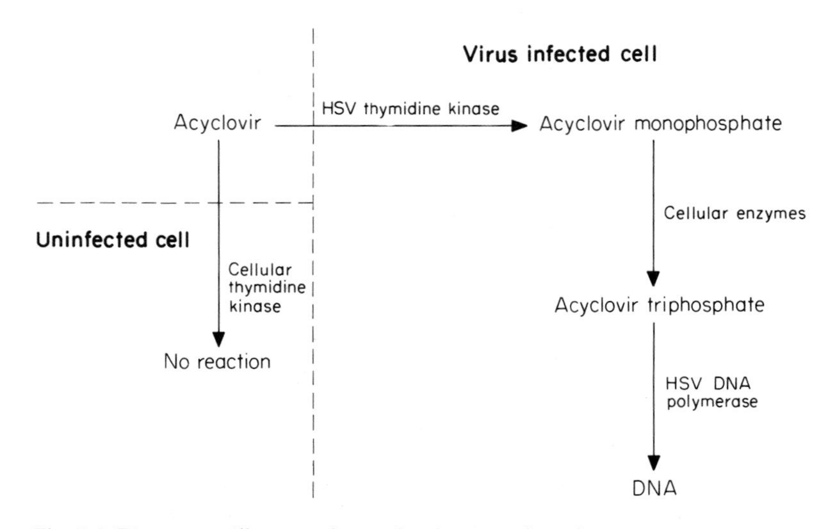

Fig. 5.3 Diagram to illustrate the mode of action of acyclovir.

may suffer severe and potentially fatal disease if they reactivate latent herpes simplex viruses. Many published trials have confirmed its value in the treatment of acute attacks of herpes simplex and varicella-zoster infections in those with normal or impaired immunity and acyclovir is the drug of choice for any clinical manifestations of these viruses which are considered to be serious enough to treat. It is important to remember, however, that it has no effect on latent virus or on the subsequent reactivation of virus from nerve ganglia. The drug is available as ophthalmic and skin/genital creams, oral and intravenous preparations.

Other drugs

Idoxuridine (IDU), cytosine arabinoside (Ara-C), adenosine arabinoside (Ara-A) and trifluorothymidine (3FT) are all nucleoside analogues (Fig. 5.4) which are non selective against herpes simplex and varicella-zoster virus infected cells. The first three have all been used systemically in the past but they have now been superseded by acyclovir. IDU, Ara-A and 3FT have therapeutic value as topical preparations for the treatment of ocular herpes simplex infections.

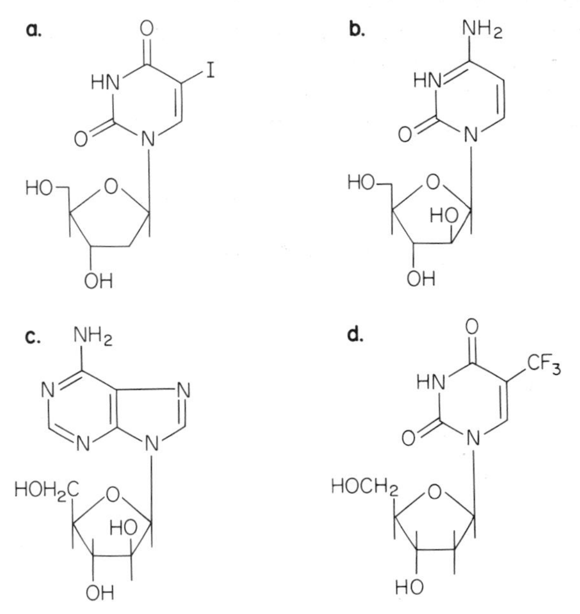

Fig. 5.4 Nucleoside analogues which have been used as antiviral agents. a = Idoxuridine (IDU); b = Cytosine arabinoside (Ara-C); c = Adenosine arabinoside (Ara-A); d = Trifluorothymidine (3FT).

Substances under evaluation

A number of potentially useful substances are currently being assessed in clinical trials. These include ribavirin (Fig. 5.5), which has shown early promise in the treatment of Lassa fever and respiratory virus infections. Dihydroxypropoxymethyl guanine (DHPG) is being used for cytomegalovirus therapy and 3-azidothymidine is on trial in HIV related diseases. (Figs. 5.6 and 5.7). Interferons which have been known since their discovery, by Isaacs and colleagues in 1957, to be active against viruses by blocking the activity of viral mRNA are now freely available as a result of genetic manipulation. Confirmation of early promise of their activity against hepatitis B virus and human papillomavirus infections is awaited.

Developments in recombinant DNA technology, the success of acyclovir and, with the advent of the AIDS epidemic, an awakening of the public to the potential of viruses as agents of epidemic disease have generated considerable activity in the search for new antiviral

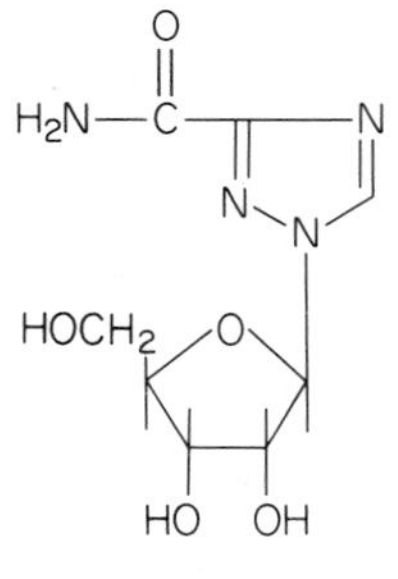

Fig. 5.5 Ribavirin.

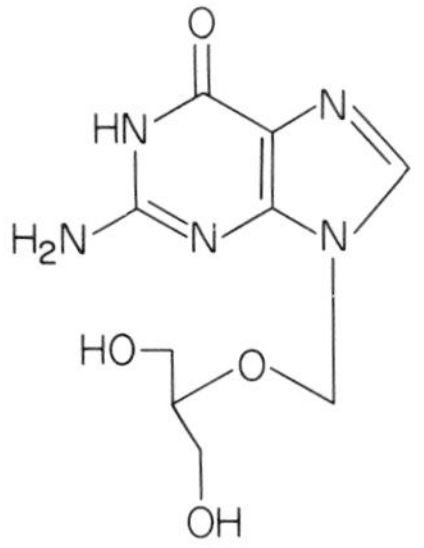

Fig. 5.6 Gancyclovir (dihydroxypropoxymethyl guanine (DHPG).

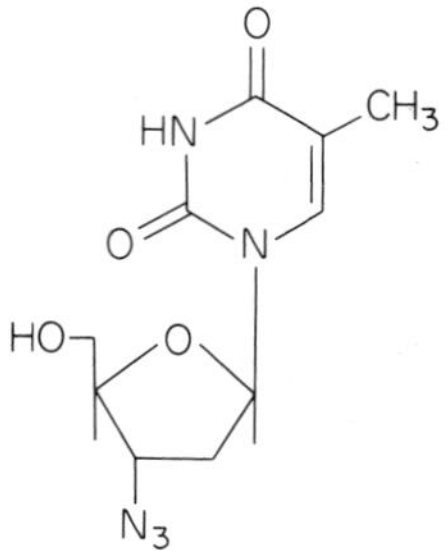

Fig. 5.7 3-Azidothymidine (AZT, zidovudine).

vaccines and drugs. This should strengthen our defences against existing diseases and any new epidemic viruses that may appear in the future but it is important to ensure that the drugs are used appropriately, and only for significant disease states, to minimize the risks of creating resistance.

Further reading

Lerner R. A. and Chanock R. M. (1984) *Modern Approaches to Vaccines*. Cold Spring Harbor Laboratory, New York.

Mims C. A. and White D. O. (1984) *Viral Pathogenesis and Immunology*. Blackwell Scientific Publications, Oxford.

Nicholson K. G. (1984) Antiviral agents in clinical practice. *Lancet*, **ii**, 503, 562, 617, 677, 736.

Oxford J. S. (1983) The prevention and control of influenza and herpes infections using specific antiviral molecules. In: *Recent Advances in Clinical Virology*, No. 3, Waterson A.P. (Ed). pp. 139–86. Churchill Livingstone, Edinburgh.

World Health Organization (1983) *Viral Vaccines and Antiviral Drugs*. WHO, Geneva.

Chapter 6
Laboratory Diagnosis

Major advances have been made in recent years in the development of diagnostic tests for viral infections. The advent of specific therapeutic agents, with the prospect of more to come, means that diagnosis must be as rapid as possible. The introduction of techniques such as electron microscopy, immunofluorescence and enzyme-linked immunosorbent assays (ELISA) for detection of viruses allows the diagnosis of many infections within hours of sample collection. Apart from the prospects of specific therapy, there are other important reasons for achieving a specific diagnosis. Demonstration of viral infection may be critical in the differential diagnosis of certain potentially life-threatening conditions such as aseptic meningitis. This disease manifestation is almost always caused by viruses (particularly enteroviruses and mumps) and is likely to resolve without therapy and with no complications. However, the syndrome is occasionally produced by infection with certain bacteria (*Mycobacterium tuberculosis, Treponema pallidum* and *Leptospira*), fungi (*Cryptococcus neoformans*) and protozoa (*Naegleria*) and these require urgent treatment with potentially toxic drugs. Another important need for rapid viral diagnosis is to prevent transmission of infection to others. Thus the demonstration of a pathogenic virus may lead to a decision to isolate the patient and/or to protect contacts by administration of immunoglobulins or vaccines.

Communication between clinical and laboratory staff is of utmost importance in viral diagnosis. This ensures that the correct samples are collected at optimal times to allow the best chance of success. By maintaining a dialogue with the microbiologist, clinical staff can then ensure that they do not miss a diagnostic opportunity that may be unrepeatable. Every virologist will recount instances of loss of potentially important information when samples taken by biopsy or surgery have been discarded or ruined for cultural purposes by immersion in formalin.

Demonstration of the presence of a virus does not, by itself, indicate a pathogenic process. The experience of the clinical virologist may be very important in assessing all the available epidemiological, clinical and laboratory evidence in deciding the importance of an isolation or serological response. Viruses isolated from faeces are often non-pathogenic whereas an agent found in a region which is normally sterile, such as the heart or brain, is likely to be the relevant pathogen. A rise in antibody may be anamnestic in response to a stimulus which may be unrelated to a virus infection; i.e. memory cells originally primed by a viral infection may be triggered to produce antibody by a non-specific effect on the immune system. This is seen in some patients with autoimmune disease and in states of virally induced polyclonal B cell activation (e.g. infectious mononucleosis and hepatitis B). To allow the clinical virologist the opportunity to interpret the results of his laboratory tests, full clinical details must be provided. It is particularly important to record the date of contact with an infected individual (if known), the date of onset of symptoms and other potentially relevant details such as foreign travel and contact with animals. This type of background information is used to determine the diagnostic tests used and, by knowing the time course of the disease, recommendations for obtaining follow-up samples at optimal times can be made. It must be remembered that, in view of the stigmata attached to certain diagnoses, there may be a need to preserve confidentiality in the display of clinical information on the request form.

Specimen collection and transport

It is important to contact the laboratory to discuss the local preferences for sample collection. Many viruses are sensitive to drying and their viability may be short lived at ambient temperatures. For this reason swabs must be placed into viral transport medium and taken to the laboratory with the minimum of delays. Many laboratories prepare their own transport medium (usually based on tissue culture medium or basic salt solution with added protein) and if a wooden stemmed cotton-wool swab is used it can be broken off into the bottle. There are also commercially available sampling kits incorporating swabs and transport medium. Swabs can be used for obtaining material from a number of sites such as the throat, skin and genital lesions, eyes, rectum, etc. but the virologist may recommend a better way of sampling from those regions. A more useful specimen from the throat may be obtained by gargling with sterile saline (in adults) or aspirating nasopharyngeal secretions with a mucus extractor (in infants). Skin samples may be better obtained by collection of fluid in capillary tubes, if vesicles are present, or by scraping or biopsy of solid lesions. Conjunctival material is usually more productive if scrapings are taken and a rectal swab is always second-best to a faecal sample. Faeces, urine, cerebrospinal fluid and other body fluids should be collected into sterile containers. Blood for culture should be collected in a sterile tube to which has been added preservative free heparin (20 i.u./ml of blood). Freezing and thawing of samples is likely to reduce the titre of any viruses present and decrease the chances of a successful isolation. For this reason, if there is likely to be a delay in processing a specimen it is usually preferable to keep it at +4°C rather than lower temperatures.

It is often possible to arrange with the laboratory to prepare slides from lesions which can then be examined at a later date by electron microscopy or immunofluorescence. This approach has enabled some laboratories to offer a service at a distance by processing samples received by post. Blood for detection of antibodies should be collected into a plain tube (without anticoagulant). Some laboratory tests (e.g. retrovirus culture) are, at present, available only in certain specialized laboratories and samples should not be sent without prior arrangement.

The clinician who takes a sample for viral investigations has a responsibility, to those who transport it and receive it in the laboratory, to ensure that it is despatched in a safe manner. A leak-proof container must be used which is firmly tightened and portering staff must be protected from the possibility of leakage. Many hospitals use a system of sealable plastic bags (which avoid the use of pins or staples which may cause inoculation injury) together with a rigid, usually metal, carrying box. Staff must be educated to understand the potential hazards present in clinical material and know the way to deal with spillages and breakages when they occur.

Diagnostic methods

The main approaches to detecting and identifying viruses present in clinical samples are illustrated in Fig. 6.1.

Direct examination of clinical material

If virus can be demonstrated in the sample as it arrives in the laboratory the result can usually be given to the clinician within a matter of minutes or hours. Although in most cases modern techni-

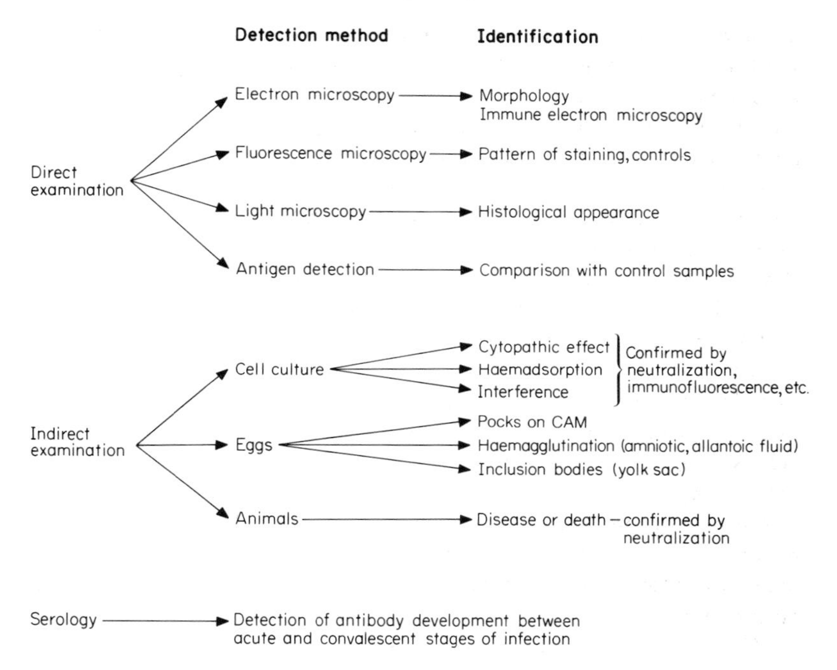

Fig. 6.1 Diagram to summarize the general approach to the diagnosis of viral infections.

ques allow a specific identification to be made the recognition of a virus from a particular family with exact characterization to follow may be enough to allow the clinician to act. Thus in the days of smallpox diagnosis, demonstration of poxvirus particles by electron microscopy, while not diagnostic of smallpox itself, was enough evidence to warrant immediate isolation of the patient and institution of other infection control measures. Herpes particles in fluid from vesicles in an immunosuppressed patient are likely to prompt the use of the drug acyclovir before they have been identified as herpes simplex or varicella-zoster.

Electron microscopy

The electron microscope has a limited but important use in diagnostic virology. It is mainly used to examine extracts of body fluids in which viral particles have been outlined, or negatively stained, by an electron-dense stain e.g. phosphotungstic acid. This technique has two main disadvantages. Because of the enormous magnification required to see viral structures there must be a large number of particles present in the sample to allow a reasonable probability that one or two may be identified. The critical number of particles necessary for the operator to find and identify the virus at a working magnification (usually × 45 000) is estimated at one million per ml of sample fluid. Another drawback is the fact alluded to above, that many different viruses have identical morphology; thus all the members of the herpes and picornavirus families are indistinguishable by negative staining. Both of these drawbacks may be resolved with the development of immune electron microscopy in which the sample is mixed with specific viral antibody. This has the effect of agglutinating the viral particles thus allowing the operator to scan at lower magnifications in search of the aggregated virions. Also if a range of suitably specific antisera are available it should be possible to identify firmly a particular serotype by reaction with its appropriate antibody.

Apart from its value (mentioned earlier) in obtaining a preliminary diagnosis (within 30 min) of herpes infection in vesicular eruptions the electron microscope has an important role in detection and identification of some viruses which cannot be cultured and for which other tests have not yet been developed. This is particularly important in examination of faeces and, following the identification of

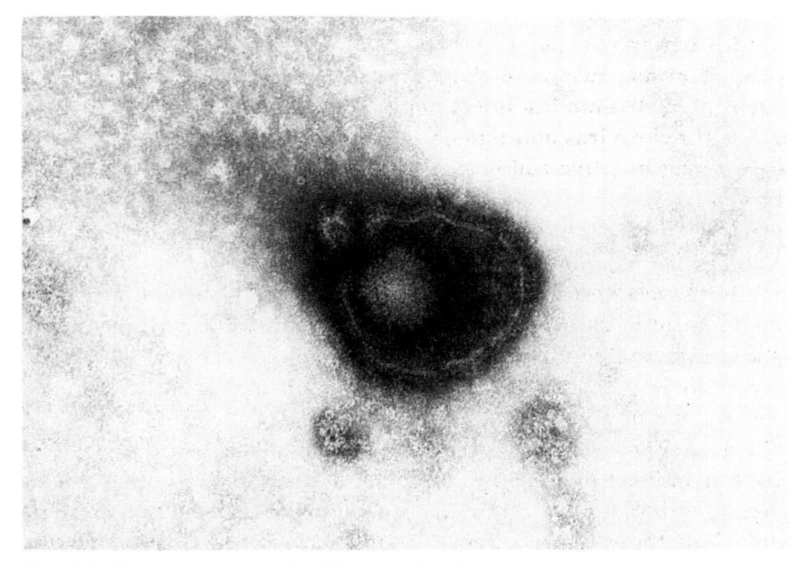

Fig. 6.2 Electron micrograph of herpes simplex virus.

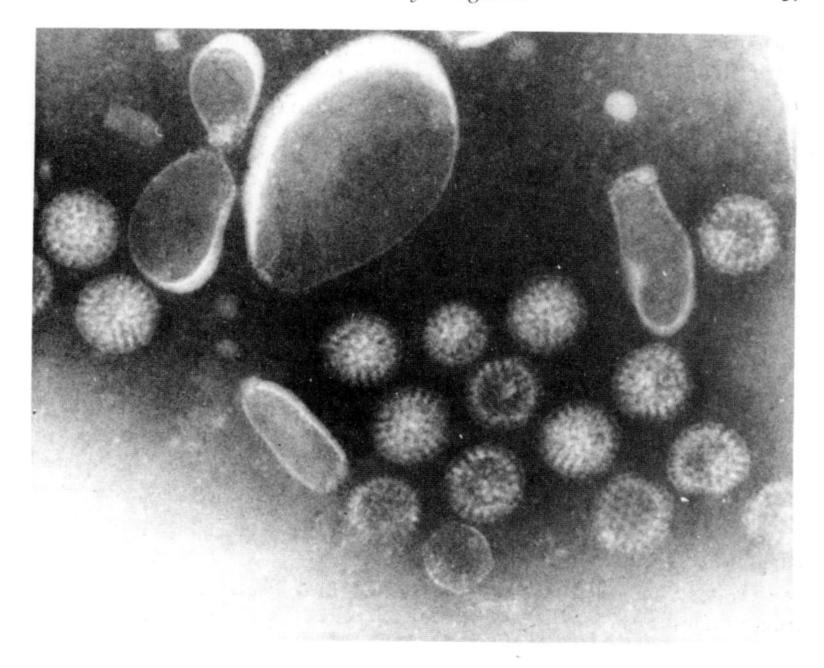

Fig. 6.3 Electron micrograph of human rotaviruses.

human rotaviruses, use of the electron microscope has lead to the recognition and means of diagnosis of a number of different viral causes of gastroenteritis (see Chapter 13). Figures 6.2 and 6.3 show herpes simplex virus and human rotavirus viewed by electron microscopy using negative staining.

Immunofluorescence

Immunofluorescence makes use of the fact that when fluorescein is viewed in ultra-violet light it fluoresces with a brilliant apple green colour. By coupling fluorescein to antibodies ultra-violet light microscopy can be used to identify antigen-antibody reactions. Smears from lesions or tissues are air-dried on slides and then fixed with chilled acetone (−20°C). They can then be stained using either the direct or indirect methods. In direct immunofluorescence (Fig. 6.4) a specific antiviral antibody is labelled with fluorescein. This is then applied to the fixed smear and after incubation and washing the specimen is mounted and examined. If virus infected cells are present

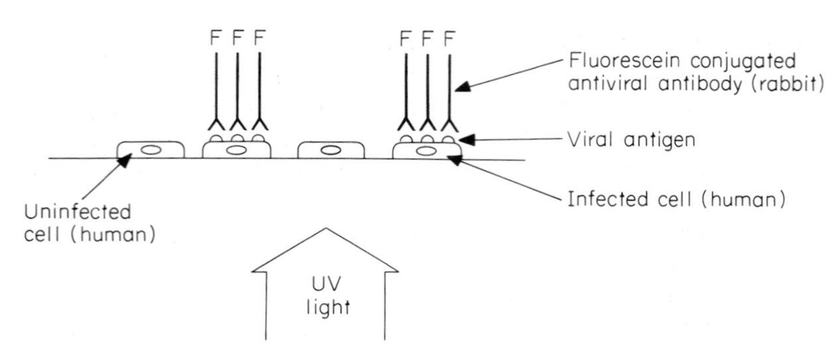

Fig. 6.4 Schematic illustration of direct immunofluorescence.

they will be stained by the labelled antibody. This only applies, of course, if the antibody used is specific for that particular virus and the need to maintain stocks of a range of fluorescein-labelled antisera limits the use of direct immunofluorescence to situations where workers are looking for infection with a single virus (e.g. rabies diagnostic centres). Indirect immunofluorescence (Fig. 6.5) has the advantage of versatility and, because of the extra step in the process which allows an increase in the ratio of fluorescein to antigen, in-

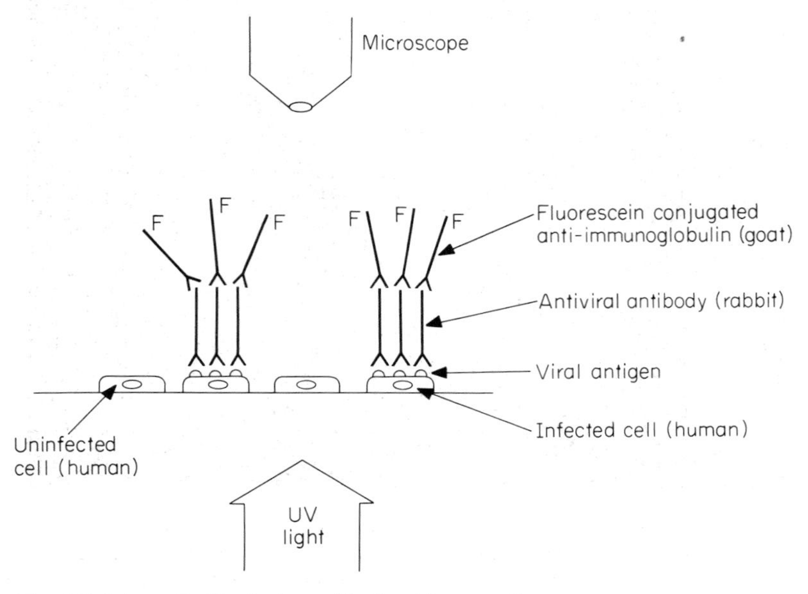

Fig. 6.5 Schematic illustration of indirect immunofluorescence.

creased sensitivity. In this technique the antiviral antibody (unlabelled) prepared in a heterologous species, e.g. rabbit, is applied to the fixed smear and then an antirabbit immunoglobulin is applied. Any cells containing viral antigens will bind the rabbit antiviral antibody and this reaction can be identified by the fluorescein-labelled antirabbit serum.

Viewed in ultra-violet light the microscopic effects of both methods are similar, the green infected cells shining out against a dark background (Fig. 6.6). As with all diagnostic tests it is critically important to incorporate a series of controls to rule out the possibility of false positive and false negative results. The reader is referred to detailed accounts of testing methods in the books listed at the end of this chapter.

Immunofluorescence is a rapid technique and results can be obtained in 1–3 hours. It has proved to be particularly useful in the identification of herpes simplex virus in brain biopsy material in

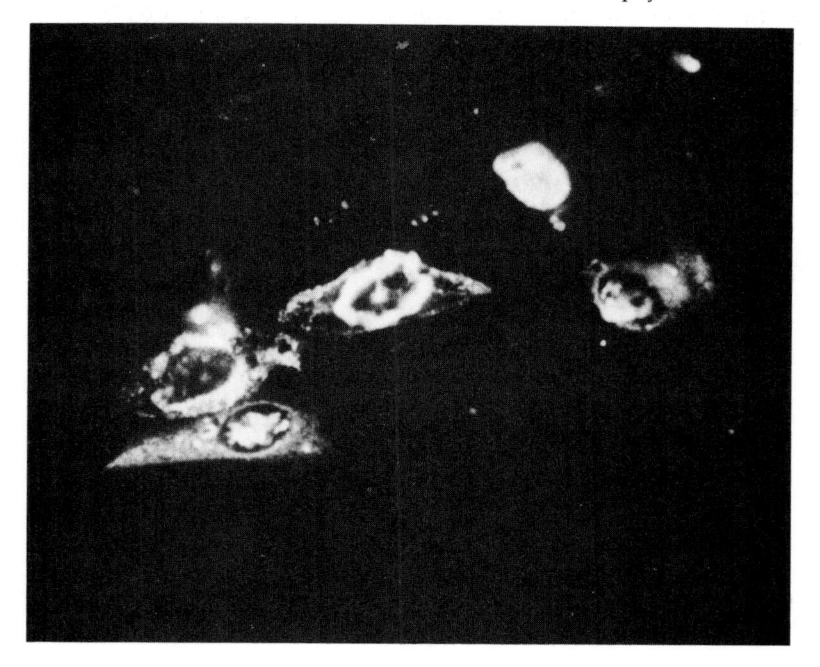

Fig. 6.6 Photograph of influenza A virus infected cells identified with a fluorescein-labelled rabbit antibody. The lighter, stained areas (which would appear apple green in a colour photograph) are present in the cytoplasm and are concentrated in the perinuclear region.

herpes simplex encephalitis, in the differential diagnosis of acute respiratory viral disease in infants and in cytomegalovirus pneumonitis in the immunocompromised. The presence of mucus in the respiratory tract may present difficulties due to non-specific fluorescence and for this reason it is sometimes preferable to inoculate the sample into a permissive cell line and then use immunofluorescence to detect early antigen production in the cultured cells.

Light microscopy

In general, the size range of viruses renders them too small to be resolved by light microscopy. It is possible to see poxvirus particles in stained preparations but no detail can be discerned. Examination of desquamated cells or tissues may, however, reveal characteristic histological changes that are diagnostic or suggestive of viral infection. As described in Chapter 4 some viruses cause inclusion formation in infected cells due to either aggregation of virions or accumulation of viral proteins. The typical 'owl eye' inclusions seen in cytomegalovirus infections (Fig. 6.7) and the intracytoplasmic Negri bodies in the hippocampus in rabies (see Fig. 4.1) are in themselves diagnostic. The presence of syncytium or giant cell formation in desquamated cell

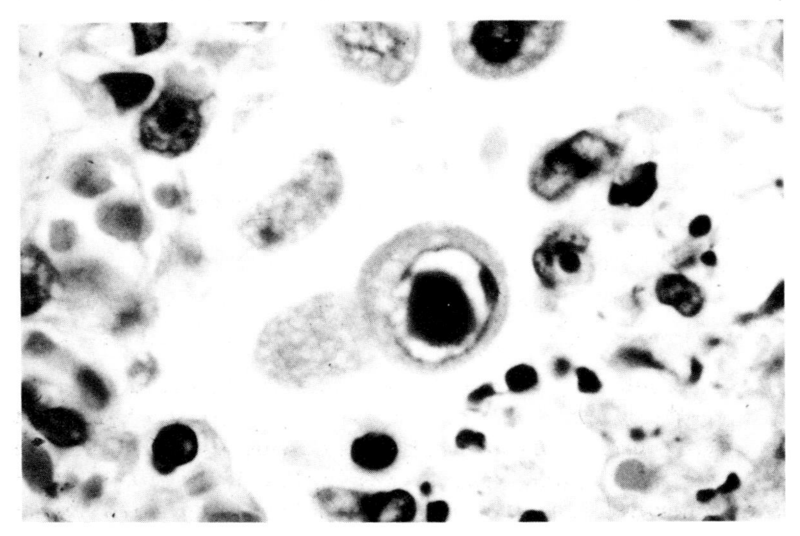

Fig. 6.7 Photograph of a cytomegalic cell. The large intranuclear inclusion and swollen nuclear membrane give the cell its characteristic resemblance to an owl's eye.

populations, or in tissues, may also give a clue to the diagnosis. Thus the presence of giant cells in the respiratory tract is characteristic of measles virus pneumonia and in a swab from the cervix uteri suggests herpes simplex infection.

Solid phase immunoassays

Sensitive assays have been developed to detect the presence of viral antigens in body fluids. The principles of the two systems used are similar (see Fig. 6.8); in radioimmunoassay (RIA) the indicator is a radioactive isotope and in enzyme linked immunosorbent assay (ELISA) an enzyme is used which activates a colour reaction. In the simplest ELISA system a specific antibody is adsorbed to the wells in a microtitre plate. The test material is then added to the wells. Any antigen present will bind to the antibody; excess is washed off. The conjugate, consisting of antiviral antibody linked to an enzyme (horseradish peroxidase or alkaline phosphatase) is added and again excess reagent is washed off. If antigen has been bound to the plate it will

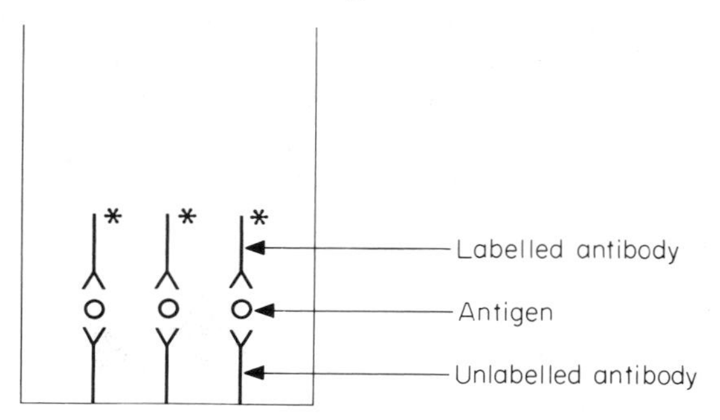

Fig. 6.8 Schematic illustration of a solid phase assay for antigen detection.

bind the antibody portion of the conjugate. Finally the substrate for the enzyme is added and the coloured product of the hydrolysed substrate is read with a spectrophotometer. This system can be made more sensitive by introducing an additional tier in the reaction. After addition of the test material an antiviral antibody prepared in another animal species (e.g. mouse) is added. The conjugate is then constructed from an antimouse immunoglobulin. RIA detection systems are similar except that the presence of antigen is assessed by counting radioactive disintegrations. Both methods have the advantage of quantitation.

Nucleic acid hybridization

Developments in molecular biology have led to the introduction of assays for viral nucleic acids in body fluids (dot-blotting). Viral DNA in a specimen is spotted on to a nitrocellulose membrane where it is bound and denatured with alkali. It is then hybridized with a radio-actively labelled viral DNA probe and autoradiographed. Similar techniques are applicable to certain RNA viruses using complementary DNA fragments transcribed from the viral RNA genome. These methods have been used successfully in the diagnosis of adenovirus, parvovirus and rotavirus infections.

Viral isolation

In situations where there is insufficient virus present in a specimen or for which there is no easily applied direct method of examination it is necessary to amplify its infectivity in a host system and obtain an isolate that can then be characterized. Even in situations where a virus can be easily detected in a rapid diagnostic test there are often considerable benefits to be gained from its isolation. Extraction of the virus in high titre enables the virologist to perform further studies which may be of clinical or epidemiological importance. A serum neutralization test using the isolate will demonstrate the development of neutralizing antibody to the patient's own virus rather than to a laboratory strain. It is also possible using restriction enzyme analysis of DNA to type the virus and this may be of epidemiological value. DNA extracted by lysis of infected cells is treated with endonucleases prepared from bacteria. These enzymes cleave the DNA at different points depending on their specificity for certain base sequences. The fragments of DNA are separated by electrophoresis in agarose and then transferred to a nitrocellulose membrane. Individual bands can be visualised by staining with ethidium bromide or, if the virus has been radiolabelled, by autoradiography. By comparing the banding pattern, two viruses can be analysed and their relationship, if any, can be assessed. Restriction endonuclease profiles of herpes simplex viruses types 1 and 2 are shown in Fig. 9.1.

Cell culture

As described in Chapter 1 viruses are obligate intracellular parasites and thus depend on living cells for their replication. The development of cell culture techniques has largely eliminated the need for animal inoculation in the isolation of viruses from clinical material. There is no universal cell line that will grow all human viruses and therefore diagnostic laboratories must maintain several different types of cell in stock cultures which are readily available to meet any diagnostic need. When a sample arrives in the laboratory the virologist decides from the clinical information which viruses are the likely causes of the patient's symptoms and the appropriate cell cultures are selected. This further emphazises the importance of providing full clinical details on the request form.

Cells are obtained from organs or tissues by initially cutting the material into small pieces and then separating the cells with proteolytic enzymes, e.g. trypsin. The isolated single cells are then resuspended in tissue culture medium which is an isotonically balanced salt solution with nutrients, buffers and serum. Many cells possess the ability to adhere to glass and plastic and this activity is enhanced by the presence of serum. After the final resuspension in medium the cells are allowed to settle on to the bottom of the container and, if they adhere, they multiply and form a cell sheet or monolayer. This provides a suitable medium for the inoculation of viruses and, as it is deposited on a transparent surface, it can be regularly inspected for evidence of virus growth. Stock cultures of cells are normally maintained in flat glass bottles or plastic flasks and cells, periodically removed by trypsinization, are seeded into smaller containers (test tubes or plastic dishes) for specimen inoculation.

Three main types of cell cultures are used for virus isolation.

Primary cells. Primary cells are obtained from the organs or tissues of adult animals and they retain the cellular characteristics of the site of origin. Many human tissues can be obtained and grown in this way but most laboratories use monkey kidney cells. These are commercially available and support the growth of many human viruses particularly enteroviruses, adenoviruses, myxoviruses, paramyxoviruses and some rhinoviruses. If attempts are made to trypsinize and reseed primary cells the secondary cultures obtained show a quite different morphology. The cells characterizing the tissue of origin which were observed in the primary culture are replaced by an overgrowth of fibroblastic cells. These may still support the growth of certain viruses but the cultures are likely to have become less sensitive to the virus for which they were originally intended.

Semi-continuous cells. These are derived from embryonic tissue and, following initial dispersal, they can be redispersed and regrown many times (usually 30–50 passages). Towards the end of this process, which may occupy a year, the cells show signs of senescence and eventually die. Human embryo fibroblasts, which are obtained from the lungs or skin and muscle tissue of embryos aborted at 10–12 weeks, provide a most valuable host system for many viruses. They are particularly valuable for isolating the herpesviruses varicella-zoster and cytomegalovirus and the latter, which is a most important pathogen, can only be grown reliably in human fibroblasts.

Primary and semi-continuous cells have a normal chromosome count (diploid) and they show the phenomenon of contact inhibition. This means that when the monolayer becomes confluent, and the cells touch each other, their growth is inhibited. The cells continue their metabolic activities but the single cell thickness is retained.

Continuous cells. Continuous cells (or cell lines) are cells that have undergone transformation to a malignant or potentially malignant state. This may occur spontaneously in culture or be initiated by mutagenic agents including tumour viruses. Malignant tissue taken from animals can often be used to establish cell lines. The cells are essentially immortal in their behaviour in culture and despite repeated passage show no signs of senescence. They do not display contact inhibition and, once a monolayer has formed, cells continue to form on top until a thick multilayered sheet is produced. The chromosome count found in different cells varies (haploid or heteroploid) and their susceptibility to viruses is likely to be different to that of the original tissue. HeLa cells and Hep-2 cells, derived respectively from a human cervical carcinoma and epithelioma are widely used and are particularly valuable for the isolation of respiratory syncytial virus.

Examples of the different types of cell cultures are shown in Figs. 6.9, 6.10 and 6.11.

Some specimens are processed to extract viruses and to remove bacteria before inoculation of cultures. Details are available in the practical books listed at the end of the chapter. The inoculum is placed on the monolayer and allowed to adsorb (usually 1 hour). It is then removed and fresh medium is added. Cultures are incubated at 37°C (33°C if rhinoviruses are being cultured) and they are inspected regularly by microscopy for evidence of virus growth. The culture medium is normally changed on the day after inoculation to minimize the effect of toxins that may be present in the inoculum, and is then replaced periodically to replenish the supply of nutrients for the

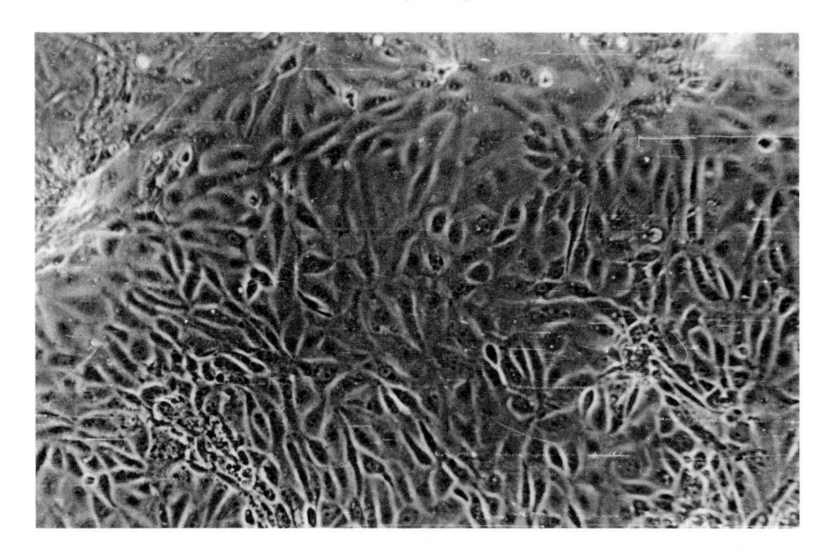

Fig. 6.9 Primary cells (monkey kidney).

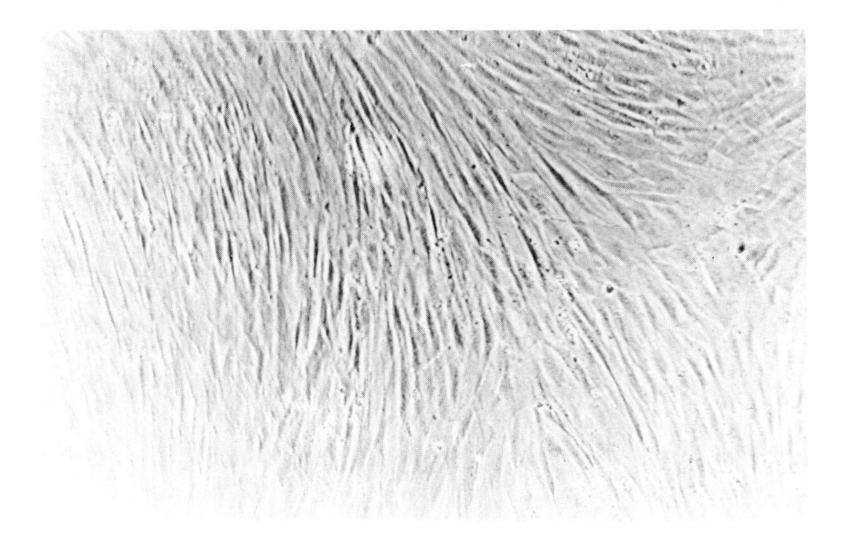

Fig. 6.10 Semi-continuous cells (human embryo fibroblasts).

cells. Cultures are incubated for varying lengths of time depending on the viruses suspected. While the cytopathic effects of a heavy inoculum of herpes simplex virus may appear overnight, a low level of

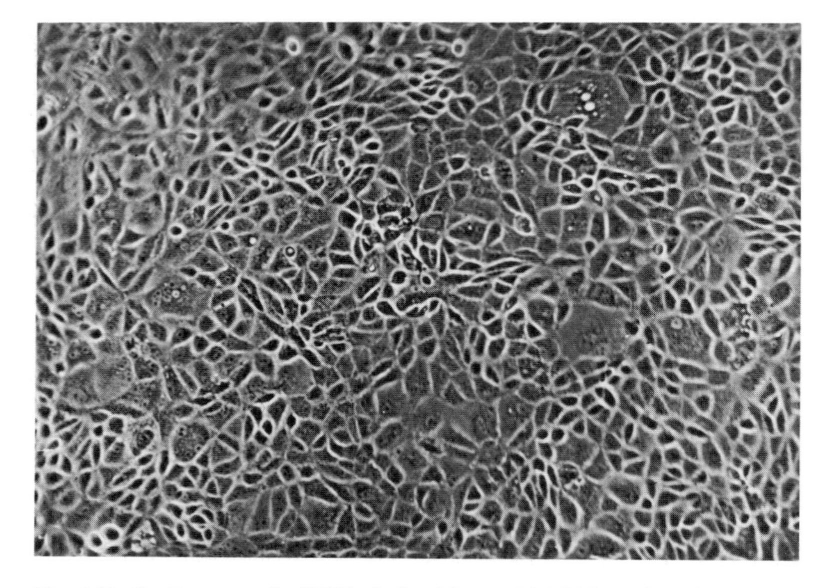

Fig. 6.11 Continuous cells (RK13, derived from rabbit kidney tissue).

cytomegalovirus may take 3–4 weeks to appear. These procedures are expensive and time-consuming and for this reason, apart from the importance to the patient, samples should be collected carefully, at optimal times and taken swiftly to the laboratory.

Detection of viruses

Many viruses are cytopathic and produce visible changes in the cell cultures. Some of these cytopathic effects (CPEs) are so characteristic, particularly when obtained from a typical clinical situation, that a diagnosis can be made on this basis alone. This is illustrated by Figs. 6.12 and 6.13 which show the typical CPEs produced by herpes simplex virus in human embryo fibroblasts and respiratory syncytial virus in HeLa cells. If a CPE cannot be readily identified, and this is the usual situation with enteroviruses, further tests are necessary. One way of proceeding is to perform a neutralization test; this involves selecting appropriate antisera in the hope of being able to neutralize the infectivity and hence block the CPE of the virus. Controlled doses of virus extracted from the original isolate are mixed

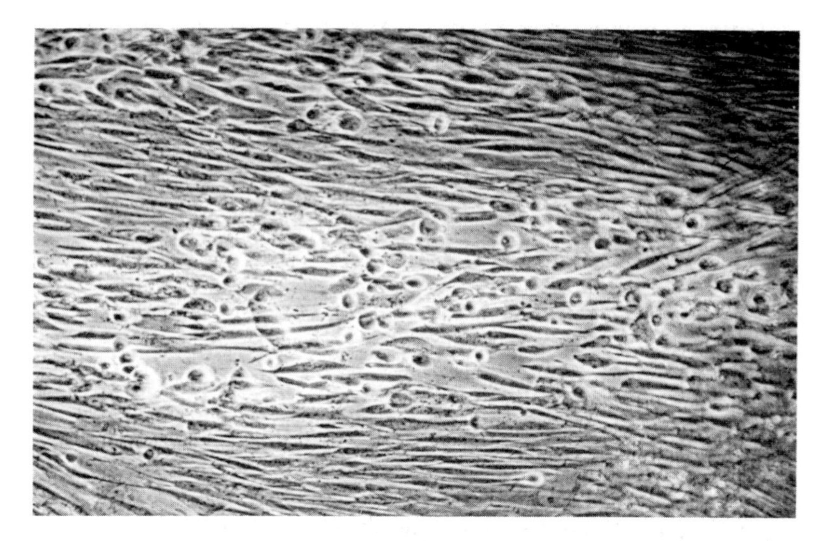

Fig. 6.12 Herpes simplex cytopathic effect in human embryo fibroblasts.

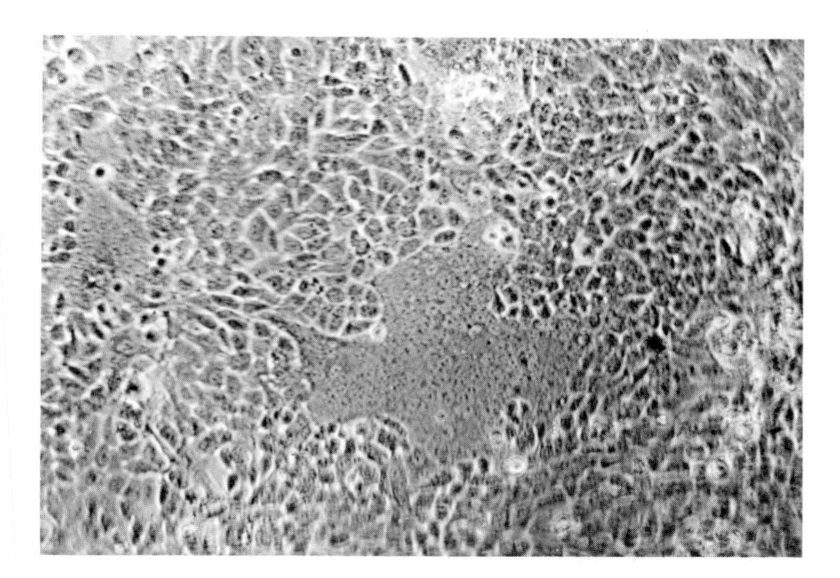

Fig. 6.13 Syncytium formation caused by respiratory syncytial virus in HeLa cells.

with different antisera and the mixtures are then inoculated into fresh tissue culture tubes. If there are many different serotypes involved the volume of work can be reduced by using pools of antisera each of which contains antibody to several serotypes. Once the virus has been neutralized by a particular pool, further neutralization tests using the individual components of that pool will identify the specific serotype involved. Other ways of identifying a cytopathic virus are to examine the cells or supernatant by electron microscopy or to apply one of the methods of antigen detection described above (immunofluorescence, ELISA or RIA) to the cultures.

Some viruses establish non-cytocidal infections in cell cultures and, if this possibility is considered, the cultures must be tested periodically to detect their presence. One way of doing this is to demonstrate the phenomenon of interference. If a virus is growing silently in a monolayer it may block the replication (probably by interferon production) of an indicator virus which is known to produce a cytopathic effect in those cells. Once detected the effect can then be neutralized. This difficult and cumbersome technique is rarely used nowadays. Immunofluorescence is a useful way of detecting the antigens produced in the cytoplasm or on the membranes of infected cells and these may be expressed early in infection and in the absence of CPE. Some viruses (particularly myxoviruses and paramyxoviruses) produce little or no CPE but produce a haemagglutinin which is expressed on the surface of the cultured cells. The presence of the haemagglutinin can be demonstrated by adding a weak suspension of erythrocytes to the monolayer. Following thorough washing, the virus infected cells can be identified microscopically by the firmly adherent erythrocytes. This phenomenon is termed haemadsorption and the haemadsorbing virus can be finally identified by a neutralization test (haemadsorption inhibition) or by immunofluorescence. The haemadsorption test is illustrated in Fig. 6.14.

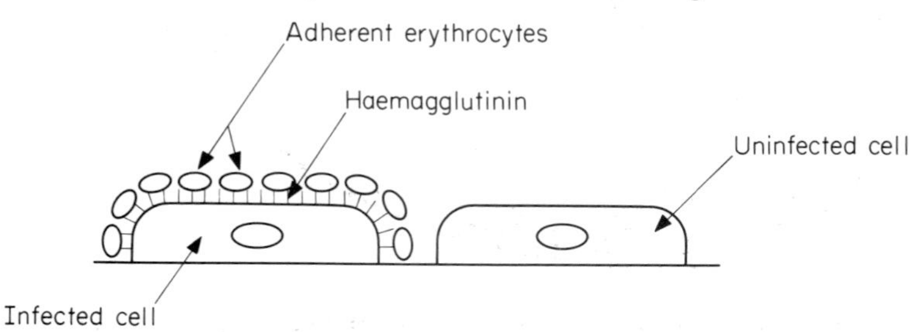

Fig. 6.14 Schematic illustration of haemadsorption.

Egg inoculation

Embryonated hens' eggs may be used for the isolation of a number of different viruses. Different regions of the egg are selected depending on the agent suspected and the eggs are pre-incubated for variable lengths of time to ensure that the membranes to be inoculated are at their most sensitive stage. Thus yolk sac inoculation is performed at an early stage of embryogenesis (8–9 days) when this structure is relatively large; more mature eggs (12–14 days) are used for chorioallantoic membrane (CAM) inoculation. The different regions of the egg that are used for virus isolation are shown schematically in Fig. 6.15. Some viruses produce visible focal lesions (pocks) on the CAM after 3 days incubation. This technique may be used as a method of distinguishing between some of the members of the orthopoxviridae. Figure 6.16 shows the typical pocks formed by vaccinia virus. Herpes simplex viruses types 1 and 2 also grow on the CAM and the lesions show a marked size difference; HSV-1 produces pin-point pocks, and HSV-2 larger pocks after 3 days (Figs. 6.17 and 6.18). The amniotic cavity is used for the primary isolation of influenza viruses and once a virus has become adapted to the hen's egg the larger allantoic cavity may be used. The presence of virus may be detected by removing fluid from the cavity and adding a weak suspension of erythrocytes.

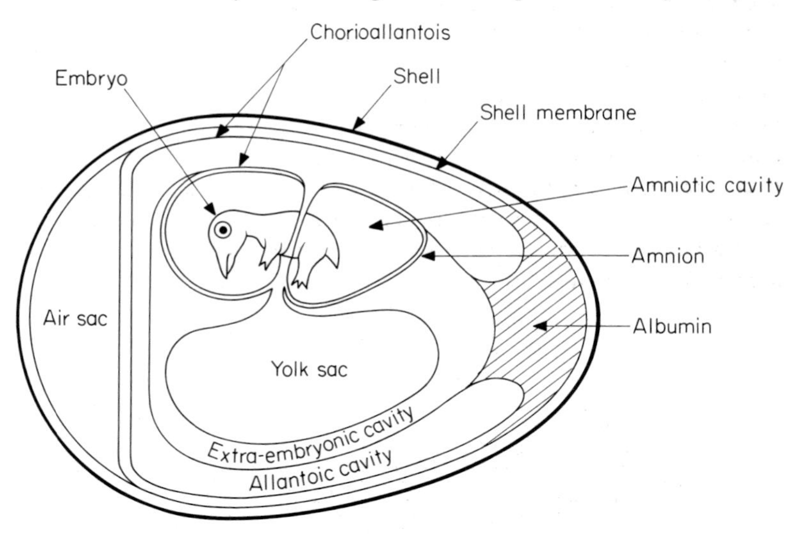

Fig. 6.15 Diagram of the fertile hen's egg indicating the regions used for propagation of viruses.

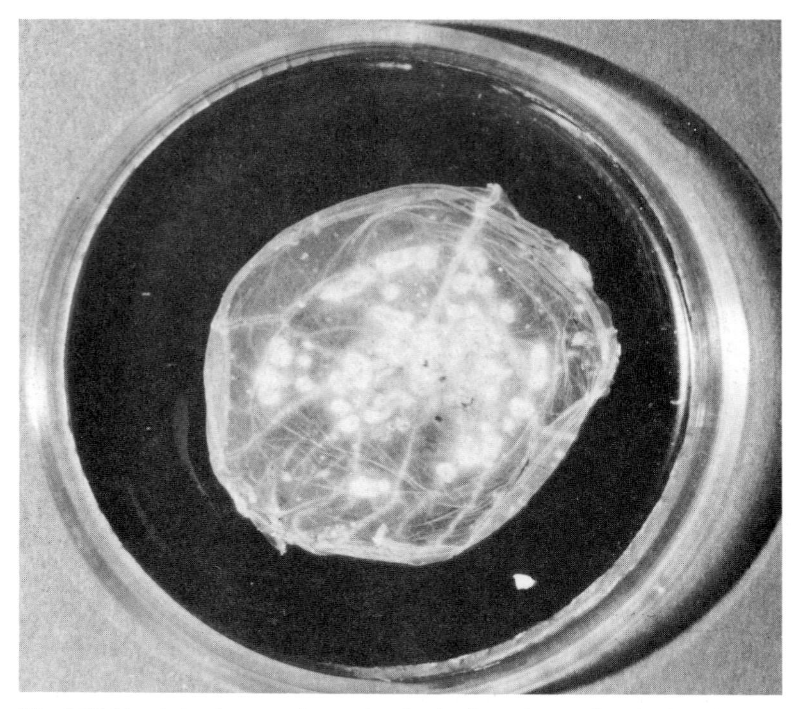

Fig. 6.16 Vaccinia virus; pocks on the chorioallantoic membrane after three days incubation.

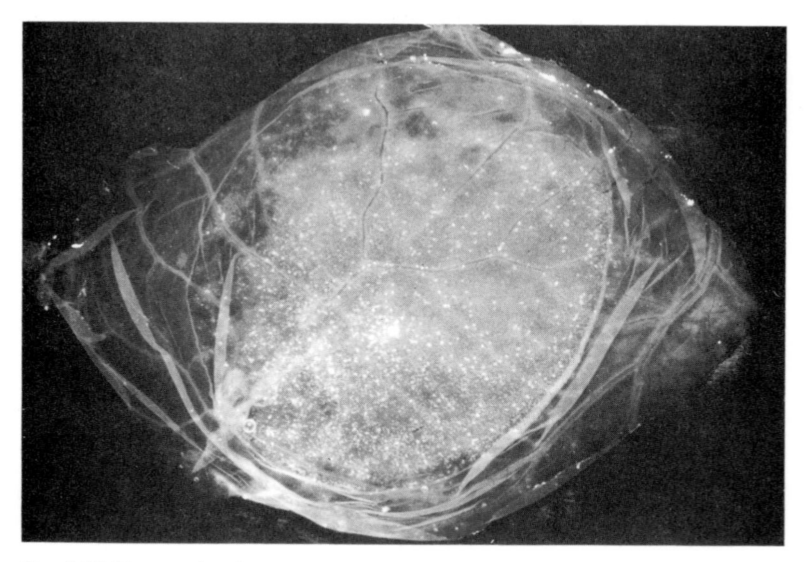

Fig. 6.17 Herpes simplex virus type 1; pocks on the chorioallantoic membrane after three days incubation.

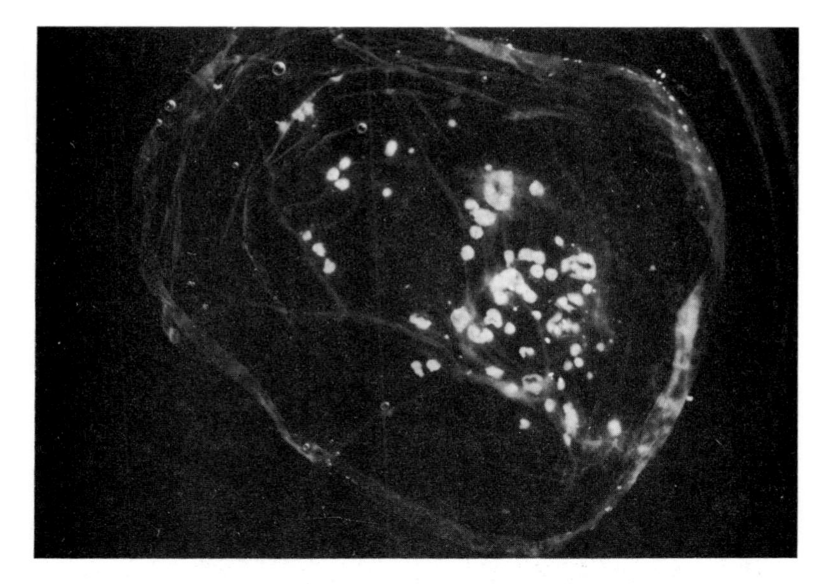

Fig. 6.18 Herpes simplex virus type 2; pocks on the chorioallantoic membrane after three days incubation.

Haemagglutination indicates the growth of a virus and this can then be finally identified by a haemagglutination inhibition test using standard antisera. The allantoic route has been of great importance in the large scale production of influenza vaccines. Yolk sac inoculation has been used for the primary isolation of rickettsiae and chlamydia.

Animal inoculation

The development of cell culture techniques has largely removed the need for animals in diagnostic virology. The main exception is the use of the suckling mouse for the primary isolation and subsequent identification (by neutralization) of group A coxsackieviruses. No satisfactory cell culture system is available for these important pathogens and their presence in clinical material is demonstrated by flaccid paralysis of newborn mice after intracerebral or intraperitoneal inoculation. This procedure is described in Chapter 11. In addition to this there is, of course, a need for animals in the production of antisera (polyclonal and monoclonal) and a requirement for certain animal products, e.g. cells, sera, complement, etc.

Serological diagnosis

When a virus infection is established in an animal host the body responds by mounting a series of immune responses. As described in Chapter 3, specific antibodies are produced by B lymphocytes and their appearance and persistence in the circulation is the basis of serological diagnosis. By selecting and standardizing purified viral antigens the presence of specific antibodies in body fluids can be detected and quantified. It must be remembered, however, that in acute viral illnesses humoral immunity takes several days to develop and a serological diagnosis is usually retrospective and achieved in the convalescent period. In chronic infections the disease may still be present when the antibodies become detectable. Viruses contain several or many structural proteins and glycoproteins and during their replication may produce a series of enzymes and other proteins. Many of these are antigenic and, therefore, a primary infection is followed by a succession of humoral responses to a range of viral antigens. As described in Chapter 3 a second exposure to a virus may result in a rapid recall of specific antibody and this may also be detected in serological tests. While a seroconversion, the appearance of specific antibody when none existed previously, usually indicates a primary infection and hence the diagnosis, a rise of at least four-fold (i.e. $<1/10-1/40$) is required for significance in serological diagnosis. In general a single serum is of little use *per se* in diagnosis although it may be all that is needed to assess whether an individual has immunity to a particular virus.

If serum can only be obtained in the convalescence phase it may still be possible to make a firm diagnosis on the basis of detection of virus specific IgM. This is described in the section on rubella diagnosis in Chapter 15. Normally the acute phase serum should be taken as soon as possible after the onset of disease and this should be followed by a further sample 2–3 weeks later. By testing the two sera in parallel significant rises in antibody may be detected. Blood samples for serology should be collected into a sterile container without anticoagulant. They may be stored overnight at 4°C and on reception in the laboratory the serum is separated by centrifugation. Serum samples are stored in the frozen state and the antibodies are reserved for many years at −20°C (or preferably −40°C).

Neutralization tests

The neutralization test was described earlier in the context of virus identification. It can also be used to obtain a quantitative assessment of neutralizing antibody in a patient's serum and by testing acute and convalescent samples this antibody can be seen to develop. The virus concerned is first titrated to obtain an exact quantitation of the infectivity present in the stock available. Then a calculated dose of the virus is prepared: normally 100 TCID 50 (100× the dilution of virus that is seen to infect 50% of the cell cultures used). The virus is then mixed with a series of serum dilutions and the mixtures are inoculated into cell cultures. The more antibody in the original serum, the more it can be diluted to neutralize the given dose of virus. One would therefore expect a significant rise in antibody between the acute and convalescent sera if the appropriate serotype of the virus has been chosen. Although very attractive in principle, this test is difficult and tedious to apply to routine diagnostic virology. It requires a large number of cell cultures and, before proceeding with the test itself, the virus(es) has to be accurately titrated. It therefore takes a long time to complete the assay. It becomes particularly tedious if there is a need to test a number of different viruses and there may be safety implications as the antigen used is the infectious virus itself. Table 6.1 shows the typical results of a virus neutralization test.

Neutralization tests can also be applied to animal isolations. If a virus has been found to produce a recognizable disease, or death, in an animal host specific antibody in a serum sample can be shown to prevent the effect of a given dose of virus from achieving this effect. Neutralizing antibody normally persists for many years and the quantitation of activity in a single serum is sometimes used to assess the need for immunization.

Table 6.1 Poliovirus neutralization test

		Cytopathic effects					
		Final serum dilutions					
Poliovirus	Serum (day of illness)	1:2	1:10	1:50	1:100	1:250	1:1250
Type 1	2	OOO	+++	+++	+++	+++	+++
	20	OOO	OOO	OOO	OOO	OO+	+++
Type 2	2	OOO	+++	+++	+++	+++	+++
	20	OOO	OOO	O++	+++	+++	+++
Type 3	2	+++	+++	+++	+++	+++	+++
	20	+++	+++	+++	+++	+++	+++
No virus	2	OOO					
	20	OOO					

Antibody to poliovirus type 1 has risen from 1/2 (acute phase) to 1/250 (convalescent phase). Minor cross-reaction has produced a slight increase in antibody to poliovirus type 2.

Complement fixation tests

Many antibodies produced in response to viral infections are complement fixing. The complement fixation test (CFT) is designed to detect the activity of these antibodies against specific viral antigens. As the patients' sera contain complement at variable levels it is essential to remove its activity before proceeding with the CFT. This is done by heating the sera at 56°C for 30 min. The CFT is dependent on two distinct antigen-antibody reactions. The first of these (test reaction) consists of the antigen for which antibodies are being detected, a dilution of the patient's serum and a known dose of complement. If there is antibody in the serum dilution it will combine with the antigen and the complement will be consumed (or fixed) in the reaction. The fixation of complement is detected by the second antigen-antibody reaction. Sheep erythrocytes coated with a complement dependent antibody (haemolysin) prepared against them are added to the system. This is known as the indicator system. If the complement was consumed in the test reaction none remains to complete the indicator reaction. The erythrocytes remain intact. If the complement was not fixed in the test system (i.e no antibody present) it becomes available to the haemolysin and enables this antibody to lyse the erythrocytes. Thus, in the CFT the presence of antibody is detected by the presence of intact erythrocytes which form a button in the testing wells, absence of antibody leads to lysis and free haemoglobin. The principle of this test is summarized in Fig. 6.19. As emphasized

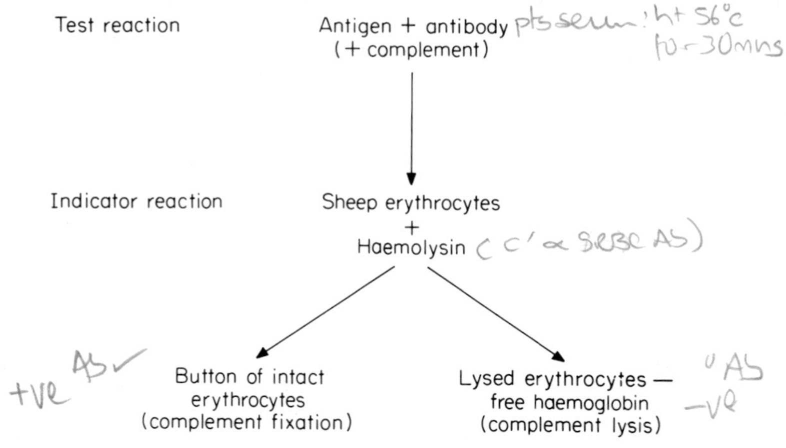

Fig. 6.19 Diagram to illustrate the steps involved in a complement fixation test.

previously in this, as in all serological tests, all the reagents must be accurately standardized beforehand and a series of controls must be included to confirm the activity and specificity of the reagents. The CFT is normally performed in microtitre plates and the first step is to place a drop of buffer in each well. Then patient's serum is placed in the first well in the row (the same volume as the buffer) and the serum is double-diluted along the row. This series of dilutions is made for acute and convalescent sera for each of the patients being tested. A drop of viral antigen is added to all the wells followed by a

Viral antigen and serum sample	Serum dilution									Results
	1:10	1:20	1:40	1:80	1:160	1:320	1:640	1:1280	1:2560	
Influenza A										
Acute	⊙	⊙	⊙	●	●	●	●	●	●	1/40
Convalescent	⊙	⊙	⊙	●	●	●	●	●	●	1/40
Influenza B										
Acute	⊙	●	●	●	●	●	●	●	●	1/10
Convalescent	⊙	●	●	●	●	●	●	●	●	1/10
Adenovirus										
Acute	⊙	●	●	●	●	●	●	●	●	1/10
Convalescent	⊙	⊙	⊙	⊙	⊙	⊙	⊙	⊙	●	1/1280
Parainfluenza type I										
Acute	●	●	●	●	●	●	●	●	●	< 1/10
Convalescent	●	●	●	●	●	●	●	●	●	< 1/10
Respiratory syncytial virus										
Acute	●	●	●	●	●	●	●	●	●	< 1/10
Convalescent	●	●	●	●	●	●	●	●	●	< 1/10

⊙ button of intact red cells = complement fixation +ve

● free haemoglobin = red cell lysis —ve

Fig. 6.20 Diagram to illustrate the appearance of a complement fixation test in which acute and convalescent sera from an individual are tested against five respiratory virus antigens. There is a significant rise in antibody (1/10 to 1/1280) suggesting adenovirus infection. Constant low titres to influenza viruses A and B are consistent with infections in the past. NB no controls are shown.

drop of complement. The plates are then placed at 4°C overnight. The indicator system is prepared by thoroughly mixing the sheep erythrocytes with the haemolysin and one drop of the mixture is added to each of the wells. The plates are shaken and allowed to settle. When the erythrocytes have formed tight buttons in the bottoms of the wells the tests are ready to be read. Figure 6.20 illustrates the appearance of a CFT plate. The antibody titre is recorded as the last well in a row to show less than 50% lysis. Although this may seem a lengthy test to perform it is, in fact relatively easily applied to large numbers of sera and can be automated. Normally a series of plates are set up in which the same sera are tested against a number of different antigens.

Haemagglutination inhibition test (HAI)

Many viruses produce a haemagglutinin and, by selecting appropriate erythrocytes and the right conditions, the phenomenon of haemagglutination (or clumping of erythrocytes) can be demonstrated *in vitro*. The haemagglutinins are antigenic and therefore antibodies are produced during the course of infection. Demonstration of these antibodies is the basis of the HAI and this test is highly specific, highly sensitive and the presence of HAI antibody correlates well with neutralising antibody. These tests are used routinely in the diagnosis of rubella and influenza infections. Before embarking on the test itself it is important to remove non-specific agglutinins and inhibitors of agglutination from the patients' sera. This can be achieved by adsorbing the sera with the erythrocytes to be used and treating the sera with kaolin or a mixture of heparin and manganese chloride. The test is performed in microtitre plates and a drop of buffer is placed in each well. A drop of the patient's serum is added to the first well and this is then carried across the plate to achieve a row of doubling dilutions. This process is repeated with acute and convalescent sera for each patient. A drop of purified haemagglutinin (or whole virus) is added to each well and after a period of incubation a drop of erythrocytes is added. The plates are shaken and the erythrocytes are allowed to settle. The pattern assumed by the erythrocytes on settling demonstrates the presence or absence of antibody in a particular well. If antibody is present, the action of the haemagglutinin will have been blocked and the erythrocytes settle into a compact button. If there is no antibody in a well, the free haemagglutinin will have clumped the erythrocytes to produce the typical peppery appearance of haemagglutination. Typical results of a test for HAI antibody are illustrated in Fig. 6.21.

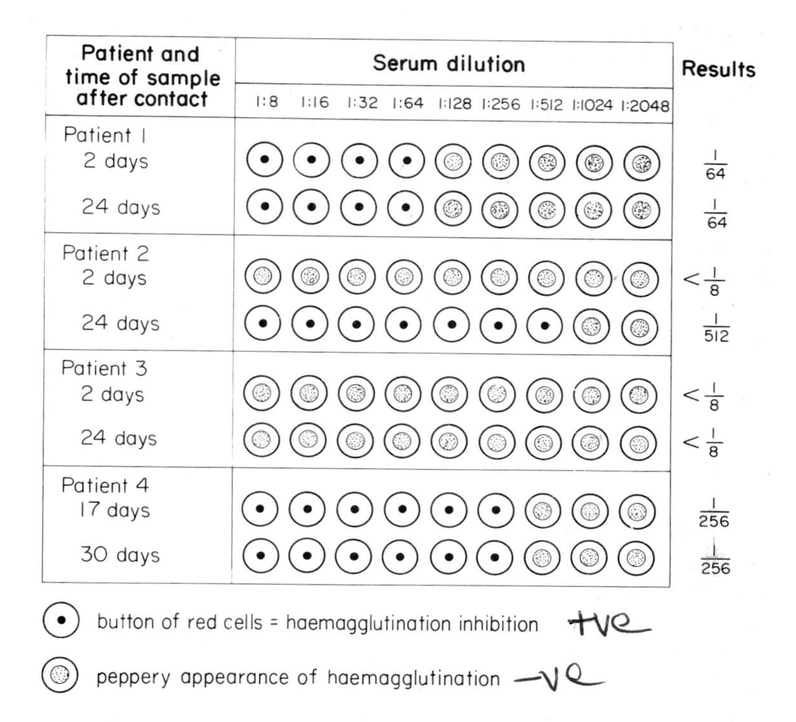

Fig. 6.21 Diagram to illustrate the appearance of a haemagglutination inhibition test. Sera taken from patients 1–3 at the second day after contact and 22 days later show different results. Patient 1 has a constant titre indicating immunity from a previous infection. Patient 2 has seroconverted demonstrating that infection has occurred and patient 3 has remained uninfected throughout. Samples from patient 4 were obtained at days 17 and 30 after contact and both have a titre of 1/256. At this stage it is impossible, from this test, to know whether this is recent or old antibody and an IgM test should be performed. NB no controls are shown.

Solid phase immunoassays

Using the techniques of ELISA and RIA described earlier in this chapter sensitive antibody tests to many different viruses have been established. In these assays the sandwich is constructed to capture specific antibody with a standard dose of a known antigen. By changing the specificity of the second antibody these solid phase assays can be adapted to measure levels of IgM, IgG or IgA. Figure 6.22 shows the details of an ELISA designed to detect rubella specific IgM.

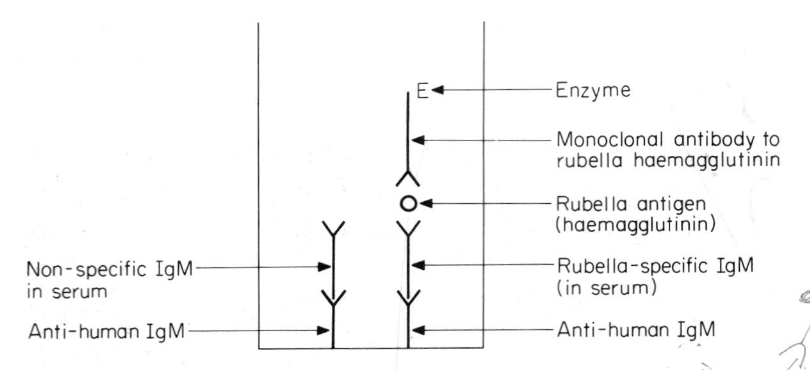

Fig. 6.22 Schematic illustration of an ELISA to detect rubella specific IgM.

Immunofluorescence

Using prepared slides on which have been deposited virus infected cells, immunofluorescence can be used to detect and quantitate anti-viral antibody. The procedure is similar to that described earlier. If end titre measurements are required, the infected monolayers are coated with a series of serum dilutions before adding the fluorescein-labelled anti-immunoglobulin. This technique can also be adapted to detecting specific IgM but, because IgG has greater affinity for the antigen than IgM, unless there is a majority of IgM present the serum must be pre-treated to remove most of the IgG.

Gel diffusion methods

Ouchterloney gel diffusion. A number of serological methods can be carried out in agar or agarose gels. The simplest of these is Ouchterloney gel diffusion. This technique was used by Blumberg in the work that led to the discovery of hepatitis B virus. Agar is melted in water and poured into a Petri dish to form a thin layer. Wells are cut in the agar and antigen and antibody are placed in adjacent wells. The plate is left to incubate for several hours and the antigen and antibody diffuse radially. When they meet they combine and if they are there in sufficient quantities they form a line of precipitation. This is a visual demonstration that an antigen-antibody reaction has taken place. The test can be used for detection of either antigen or antibody. Its disadvantage is its low level of sensitivity but a major asset of this test lies in the fact that, if two antigens in adjacent wells react with the same antibody, the precipitation lines may totally fuse.

This pattern, known as the line of identity, indicates that the antigens are identical. The layout and precipitation patterns are illustrated in Fig. 6.23.

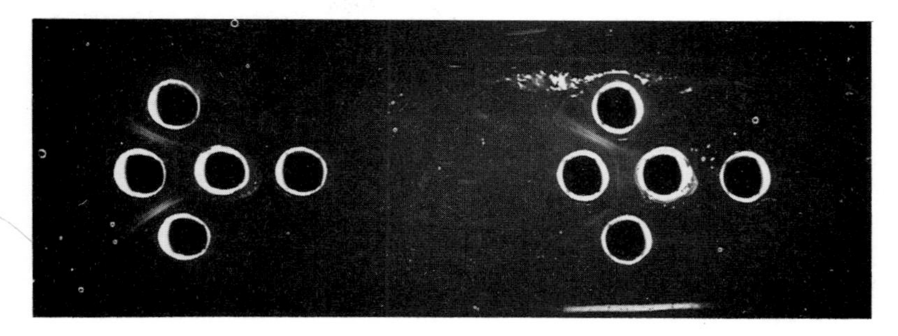

Fig. 6.23 Ouchterloney gel diffusion showing precipitin lines of complete and partial identity.

Counter-immunoelectrophoresis. The sensitivity of gel diffusion can be enhanced by passing an electric current through the well. By using

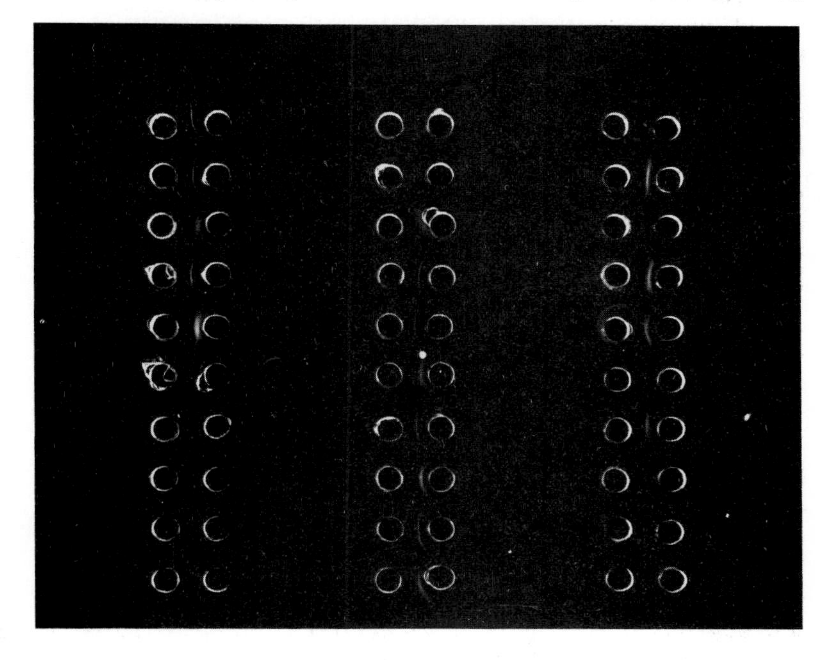

Fig. 6.24 Counter-immunoelectrophoresis showing lines of precipitation of antigen and antibody.

appropriate buffers a negative charge can be applied to an antigen which moves towards the anode. The antibody migrates with the endosmotic flow of electrolytes and liquid and, where the two components meet, a precipitin line forms (Fig. 6.24).

Single radial haemolysis. A highly sensitive gel system has been developed which is of great importance for screening large numbers of sera for antibodies to certain haemagglutinating viruses. It has been adopted as a routine test for rubella antibody to determine immune status as a prelude to active immunization. A thin layer of agarose, containing sheep erythrocytes, rubella agglutinin and complement is layered in a Petri dish. The agarose used has a low setting temperature so that the erythrocytes are not lysed during the preparation.

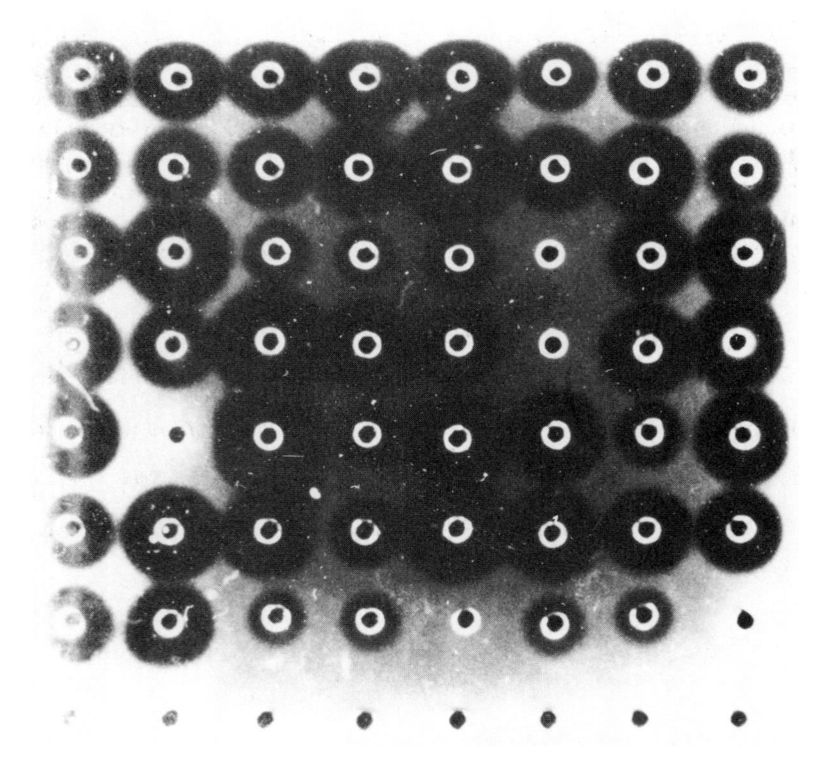

Fig. 6.25 Radial haemolysis tests for rubella antibody. Note the areas of lysis around the wells; their diameter is proportional to the level of antibody present in the serum.

Wells are cut in the gel and a drop of patient's serum is placed in each well. Control sera, containing a level of antibody that is on the borderline for protection, are added to other wells. The rubella haemagglutinin combines with the erythrocytes in the gel and, despite the presence of complement, the cells retain their integrity. When serum is placed in a well, it starts to diffuse radially. If there is specific antibody in the serum it will combine with the agglutinin on the erythrocyte membrane and, in the presence of complement, lysis will occur. Thus a well containing a positive serum will be surrounded by a clear halo which indicates that the erythrocytes have been lysed. This result is demonstrated in Fig. 6.25. The diameter of the zone of lysis is directly related to the titre of antibody present in the serum. If the zone has a greater diameter than the control serum the individual is immune to rubella.

A number of other indicator systems have been devised to detect antigen-antibody reactions and the range of tests is constantly being extended. It must be remembered, however, that humoral immunity is only one part of a very complex range of responses to viral infections and in many it is probably not a major part. It is to be hoped that technological advances will enable diagnostic laboratories to routinely test for cell-mediated responses to infection and this may be particularly important in assessing the success of immunization.

Further reading

Gardner P. S. and McQuillan J. (1980) *Rapid Virus Diagnosis*. Butterworths, London.

Grist N. R., Ross C. A. and Bell E. J. (1974) *Diagnostic Methods in Clinical Virology*. Blackwell Scientific Publications, Oxford.

Kurstak E. and Kurstak C. (1977) *Comparative Diagnosis of Viral Disease*. Academic Press, New York.

Versteeg J. (1985) *A Colour Atlas of Virology*. Wolfe Medical Publications, London.

Chapter 7
Respiratory Infections

The respiratory tract is very vulnerable to infection with many different types of viruses and the pattern of disease produced depends on the virus, the site of infection, immunity remaining from previous exposure to the same or related viruses and the age and general resistance of the host. Infections occur throughout life but they are likely to be particularly severe in the very young and the elderly. The presence of underlying chronic lung diseases (e.g. cystic fibrosis, chronic bronchitis and bronchiectasis) may precipitate severe disease during acute viral respiratory infection. The defence mechanisms which operate in the respiratory tree were described in Chapter 2 and as previously indicated cigarette smoking, which paralyses the action

Table 7.1 Viral respiratory diseases

Disease	Viruses
Rhinitis	Rhinoviruses, adenoviruses, coronaviruses, parainfluenza viruses, influenza viruses, respiratory syncytial virus, some coxsackie A viruses
Pharyngitis/tonsillitis	Adenoviruses, parainfluenza viruses, influenza viruses, rhinoviruses, coxsackie A or B viruses, herpes simplex viruses, Epstein–Barr virus
Stomatitis	Herpes simplex viruses, some coxsackie A viruses
Laryngotracheobronchitis	Parainfluenza viruses, influenza viruses, adenoviruses
Bronchitis	Parainfluenza viruses, influenza viruses, respiratory syncytial virus, adenoviruses, measles virus
Pneumonia	Influenza viruses, parainfluenza viruses, adenoviruses, respiratory syncytial virus (infants), varicella-zoster virus, measles virus. Cytomegalovirus and herpes simplex viruses in the immunocompromised

of the cilia, promotes the spread of inflammation. The major causes of viral respiratory infection are listed in Table 7.1.

Viral diseases are normally described as involving the upper or lower respiratory tracts (or both). The arbitrary dividing line between the upper and lower regions is normally taken as the laryngo-tracheal junction.

Rhinoviruses

The rhinovirus group are members of the picornavirus family and differ from enteroviruses in being acid-labile, in having an optimal growth temperature of 33°C (rather than 37°C) and a buoyant density in caesium chloride of 1.40 (compared to 1.34). There are known to be more than 110 different serotypes of rhinoviruses and there is evidence from field and laboratory studies of antigenic variation and generation of new types. They are prevalent throughout the world with epidemics, in temperate climates, being particularly common in the autumn and spring. They can be very readily transmitted at these times and may spread to infect 80–90% of the members of a confined institution such as a school. In tropical areas they predominate in the rainy season. There are usually several serotypes circulating and causing disease at the same time. All ages are susceptible and the frequency ranges from 1.2 attacks per year in infants to 0.7 in adults. Rhinoviruses are spread by direct and indirect contact. The role of viral contamination of the hands from infected individuals or from fomites and subsequent autoinoculation of the respiratory tract or conjunctivae is probably significant and is underestimated as a route of transmission.

The incubation period is one to four days and virus can be isolated from nasal secretions at the time of onset of symptoms. Disease is mainly confined to the nasal mucosa (including the sinuses) and nasopharynx and this localization is attributed to the fact that virus growth is inhibited at 37°C. The virus spreads from cell to cell in the mucosa and the resulting cellular damage leads to acute inflammation, oedema with associated nasal obstruction and nasal discharge. These local effects produce the predominent features of a head cold or coryza and although there may be other effects including malaise, headache, sore throat and cough, these are usually mild. Fever is unusual in rhinovirus infection. Damage to the mucosa of the sinuses and middle ear may lead to super-added bacterial infection and another complication of rhinovirus infection is the precipitation of acute bronchospasm in asthmatics. Recovery from infection is attributed to specific IgA production and probably also local interferon. Reinfection with the same serotype can occur but this is uncommon.

Laboratory diagnosis

Rhinoviruses can be grown in human embryo fibroblasts; some serotypes grow in monkey cells. The cell cultures are maintained at 33°C and are normally grown in tubes in roller apparatus. They may also be isolated in explants of ferret or human epithelium and the growth of virus may be detected by the cessation of ciliary action on the mucosal surface. Because of the large number of serotypes, antibody testing is not normally attempted by diagnostic laboratories.

Management

No specific therapy or vaccines are available and treatment, if necessary, is symptomatic and involves relief of nasal obstruction. Antibiotics and bronchodilators may be required to combat the complications described above.

Coronaviruses

Members of the Coronaviridae cause head colds in humans and the clinical effects are similar to those of rhinoviruses. They have not been associated with lower respiratory tract disease. At least three serotypes are involved. There is no specific therapy and no vaccine.

Adenoviruses

There are at least 39 serotypes of human adenoviruses and they are particularly associated with sore throats. They were originally discovered as passenger viruses in the adenoids of young children, removed at adenoidectomy for nasal obstruction, and certain serotypes (1, 2, 5 and 6) are present for long periods in up to 30% of children. These asymptomatic infections are present in a very small number of cells and do not normally represent an infectious risk to others. Epidemics of infection occasionally arise and at those times a single serotype predominates. When this occurs, children are usually infected with types 1, 2, 3, 5 and 7 and adults with 4 and 7.

The major symptom of adenovirus infection is usually acute pharyngitis but extension of the disease to involve the lower respiratory tract is not unusual. Pneumonia is an occasional complication in infants, children and young adults. The syndrome of pharyngoconjunctival fever is sometimes seen in epidemic form; it is usually caused by adenovirus type 3 and may be acquired in swimming pools. It should be noted that, unlike rhinoviruses, adenoviruses grow optimally at 37°C and are acid-stable. For these reasons they may invade the lower respiratory tract and can also infect the gastrointestinal tract. The upper respiratory effects are often accompanied by abdominal pain and in some individuals the pain can be localized to tender, enlarged mesenteric lymph nodes. This finding indicates intestinal infection (mesenteric adenitis) and if the pain is maximal in the right iliac fossa it may mimic acute appendicitis. In infants the presence of hypertrophied lymphoid tissue, either in the bowel wall or attached to it, may lead to enhanced peristalsis in an effort to remove what is recognized as a foreign body. Invagination of the bowel may result and the gangrene developing from intussusception will require emergency surgery.

Laboratory diagnosis

Adenoviruses grow well in human cell cultures particularly human embryo kidney and continuous lines (e.g. HeLa) to produce a characteristic CPE. The common group antigen is used to demonstrate rises in antibody; the complement fixation test has been used extensively for this purpose.

Management

No specific therapy exists but a vaccine against types 4 and 7 has been highly effective in military recruits in the United States. The live vaccine incorporates both serotypes in an enteric-coated capsule and produces an asymptomatic intestinal infection without respiratory effects.

Influenza viruses

Influenza viruses are the only members of the Orthomyxoviridae. There are three subtypes of influenza and many different antigenic variants of influenza A and B (see Table 7.2). Influenza C has not been shown to vary antigenically to any marked extent and, although it

Table 7.2 Human influenza viruses

Type	Subtype	Years of prevalence	Representative variants
A	H1N1	1918–1957	A/Puerto Rico/8/34 A/FM/1/47
	H2N2	1957–1967	A/Japan/305/57
	H3N2	1968–	A/Hong Kong/1/68 A/Victoria/3/75 AS/Texas/1/77 A/Bangkok/1/79
	H1N1	1977–	A/USSR/92/77 A/England/333/80
B	None defined	1940– (date first isolated)	B/Hong Kong/5/72 B/Singapore/222/79
C	None defined	1949– (date first isolated)	C/JHB/2/66

infects the human, is not normally symptomatic. Antigenic variants result from the processes of antigenic shift (major changes) and antigenic drift (minor changes). In antigenic shift, a new variant appears in which one (or both) of the surface antigens (haemagglutinin and neuraminidase) shows no serological reaction with those of recently existing strains. This is thought to result from a recombination of two influenza strains. Antigenic shift has only been observed with influenza A viruses and, in recorded history, has occurred three times in the haemagglutinin and twice in the neuraminidase. The resulting antigens have been designated H1, H2, H3, N1 and N2. Antigenic drift results from mutations in the RNA genome of the viruses and is recognized by a reduction in serological reactivity between new isolates and recently prevalent strains. The new variant is identified by the type, location of first isolation, specimen number and year of isolation (e.g. B/Singapore/222/79).

Influenza viruses are major causes of respiratory disease and this shows different epidemiological patterns depending on the type of virus and the degree of antigenic change from previous strains. The pattern may be pandemic (i.e. worldwide), epidemic or endemic. Pandemic influenza has only been seen with influenza A as it requires antigenic shift to render the entire world susceptible to infection. Recent pandemics occurred in 1889, 1918, 1957 and 1968. With antigenic drift, a portion of the population becomes susceptible and, as this pool becomes larger, an epidemic threatens. The transmission of influenza is favoured by the accessibility of susceptibles to infected individuals in closely confined areas together with high humidity and poor ventilation. The accessibility and high speed of modern aircraft leads to the rapid dissemination of new variants throughout the world.

Influenza is normally transmitted by aerosols and viral particles are deposited in the respiratory mucus. The virus binds to neuraminic acid in the mucoprotein, but the particle-associated neuraminidase releases it. The resulting liquefaction of mucus may allow the virus to come into contact with mucosal cells where it can bind by means of the haemagglutinin.

The incubation period of influenza is one to five days and infectious virus is present in the nasopharynx towards the end of this time. A spreading destruction of the respiratory epithelium results in inflammation, oedema and mononuclear cell infiltration throughout much of the respiratory tree. The clinical features of typical influenza (A or B) start with fever, headache and myalgia associated with nasal discomfort, sore throat and a non-productive cough (often painful due to tracheitis). The systemic effects normally subside in two to four days but the respiratory symptoms may persist for several days longer. Although viraemia has been reported in influenza it is rare and is unlikely to account for the toxic effects experienced early in the disease. These have been attributed to endogenous pyrogen release from phagocytes and the formation of circulating immune complexes. With the advent of cloned interferons, the similarity of interferon toxicity to the systemic effects of influenza suggests that the body's interferon response may be contributing to the illness. Influenza causes considerable lassitude at the acute stage and marked debility and sometimes depression during convalescence. Although interferons may be important in recovery from the disease, humoral antibody (IgA and IgG) is the main protection against reinfection. Haemagglutination inhibiting antibody is the key to this defence.

Antineuraminidase antibody impairs virus release from cells and is important in determining the degree of illness caused by the virus. The danger of influenza lies in its complications. In infants, as with parainfluenza viruses, it may precipitate croup (see below). In anyone with chronic lung disease, the development of widespread acute inflammation is likely to lead to secondary invasion with pathogenic bacteria. This may result from damage to the barrier normally provided by the mucous membranes together with impairment of ciliary action. In addition to this, however, is the likelihood that phagocytic function is directly inhibited by the virus (see Chapter 3). These are probably the reasons for the dangerous complication of staphylococcal pneumonia occurring as a result of acute influenza. Influenza viruses may also directly invade lung tissue to cause a viral pneumonia without the obvious contribution of opportunistic bacteria; this may be rapidly fatal.

Laboratory diagnosis

Rapid diagnosis can be achieved by immunofluorescence either on desquamated cells present in the respiratory tract or by detection of early antigen in infected cell cultures. The presence of virus growing silently in monolayers can also be demonstrated by haemadsorption (see Chapter 6). The amniotic cavity of the embryonated hen's egg provides a sensitive culture system, the presence of virus being ascertained by testing samples for haemagglutination with guinea pig erythrocytes. Complement fixation tests employ the internal nucleoprotein antigen which is antigenically stable and are useful for establishing that a patient has recently suffered from the disease. Haemagglutination inhibition tests for antibody (using whole virus as the antigen) are highly sensitive and specific. By using this technique, the minor variants of the viruses can be distinguished.

Prevention and treatment

Vaccines are available which incorporate the currently prevalent strains of influenza A and B. Because of recent circulation of H3N2 and H1N1 concurrently, antigens from both of these types have been included, in the vaccines. In recent years subunit vaccines, which contain purified haemagglutinin and neuraminidase, have been introduced and these lessen the danger of hypersensitivity reactions to nucleoprotein antigens of the virus. The vaccines, which protect approximately 70% of recipients, are recommended for elderly and debilitated individuals and particularly those with chronic cardiovascular and/or pulmonary disease. The chemotherapeutic agent, amantadine, has been shown to have prophylactic and therapeutic activity against influenza A (but not influenza B). In trials conducted in adults and children it prevented infection to approximately the same extent as the vaccines. Amantadine has also been shown to produce a reduction in the intensity and duration of symptoms of acute influenza. Although early studies of its use in influenzal pneumonia were disappointing, further data are needed.

Paramyxoviruses

Respiratory syncytial virus (RSV) and parainfluenza viruses (types 1–3) are important respiratory pathogens. They can infect and cause disease at any age and reinfection is common but, while minor illness usually results in older children and adults, they may produce serious disease in the very young. In temperate climates parainfluenza viruses show both epidemic and endemic patterns of infection; RSV is epidemic in winter. Transmission by contact with respiratory secretions has been demonstrated and fomites may play an important role in this; the significance of small particle aerosols has not been determined. The incubation periods vary between two and five days and spreading mucosal damage leads to acute inflammation with oedema and lymphocytic infiltration.

RSV is the major cause of bronchiolitis which occurs in infants in the first year of life. Dyspnoea is the predominant effect of this virus and this is clearly evident from inspecting the infant's chest. Rapid respiration is accompanied by intercostal and subcostal recession and in addition to this the accessory muscles of respiration in the neck may be active. There is usually a dry, troublesome cough and, on percussion of the chest, the lung fields are hyper-resonant due to air trapping. Figure 7.1 shows the radiological appearance of an infant with acute bronchiolitis. Note the flattening of the diaphragm and increased translucency of the lung fields. There is often little to hear on auscultation and there is usually little or no wheezing. The illness may be complicated by extension of the virus to lung tissue to produce a viral pneumonia and there may also be the added complication of cardiac failure. Neonatal infections vary in severity but some infants develop pneumonia which may be life-threatening. RSV frequently causes apnoeic attacks in the neonate, particularly if the baby is premature. This observation, together with the presence of viral antigen in the lungs of some babies, has led to the suggestion that some cases of the sudden infant death syndrome (SIDS) may be caused by RSV.

Parainfluenza viruses are the main cause of viral croup although this condition may also be due to influenza viruses and adenoviruses. Croup is characterized by a barking, metallic cough and noisy inspirations (inspiratory stridor). This complication usually follows on from a febrile upper respiratory tract infection. The onset of noisy respiration usually occurs at night and is alarming to the patient and the parents. Parainfluenza viruses (like influenza) cause an acute laryngotracheobronchitis which results in oedema and swelling of the

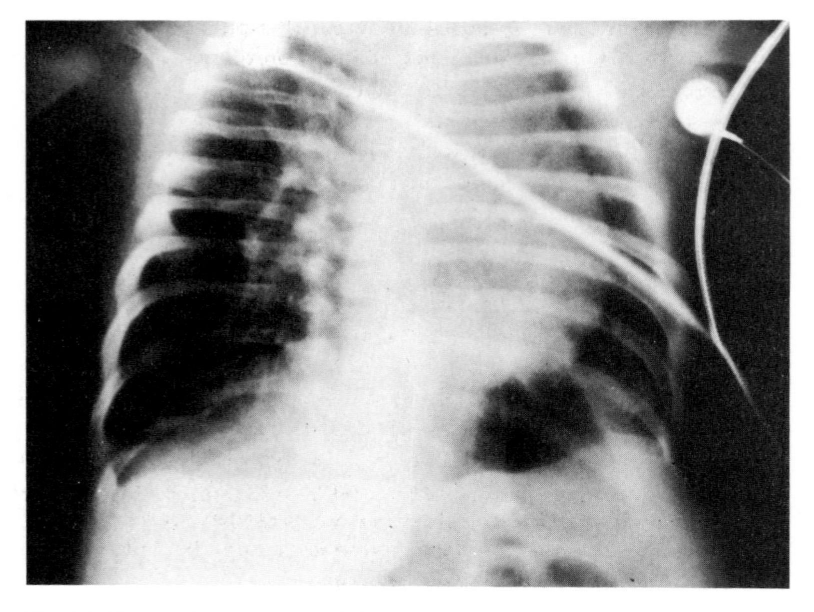

Fig. 7.1 Chest radiograph of an infant with acute bronchiolitis caused by respiratory syncytial virus. Note the increased translucency of lung fields and lowering of the diaphragm which indicate air trapping and hyperexpansion of the chest.

submucosa. The commonest age for croup is 18 months, and at this time, the diameter of the sub-laryngeal airway is narrower than at any other time in life. The respiratory obstruction is, therefore, likely to occur at this point at this vulnerable age. The stridor resulting from viral croup must be differentiated from other infectious causes of obstruction to the large airways. Diphtheria produces a dry croup which develops slowly and can be recognized by the characteristic grey membrane which obstructs respiration and can usually be seen at the back of the throat. Respiratory obstruction due to the oedema associated with acute epiglottitis is caused by *Haemophilus influenzae* (capsule type B) and is dramatically sudden in onset. This complication of *Haemophilus influenzae* septicaemia may present as an acute emergency and immediate tracheotomy may be life-saving.

Laboratory diagnosis

As with influenza viruses, rapid diagnostic tests employing immunofluorescence provide a diagnosis within 2–3 hours if the sample is examined directly or 1–2 days if the material is put into cell culture. Virus growth can be confirmed by observation of syncytium formation due to RSV or by haemadsorption in the case of parainfluenza viruses. Complement fixation tests for antibody using antigens prepared from RSV and each of the parainfluenza virus types are useful in the differential diagnosis of acute respiratory disease.

Management

There are no vaccines or chemotherapeutic agents for these viruses in routine use although ribavirin is being evaluated in RSV infection. Supportive therapy is the key to success in managing infected infants and, provided they survive the acute stage, they normally recover without sequelae. Oxygenation and ventilatory support when necessary are combined with close observation to detect and treat bacterial superinfection. If cardiac failure develops digitalization will be required. Humidification of the inspired air and sedation are beneficial in viral croup and, in contrast to diphtheritic croup, the child usually recovers without the need for tracheotomy.

Atypical pneumonia

Atypical pneumonia is classically caused by *Mycoplasma pneumoniae* but several other agents may produce a similar clinical picture. These include *Coxiella burnetii* (Q fever), *Chlamydia psittaci* (psittacosis/ornithosis) and *Legionella pneumophila* (Legionnaires disease). All of these agents may produce a severe pneumonia which, without appropriate treatment, may on occasion be fatal. While it is beyond the scope of this book to cover the details of these rickettsial, chlamydial and bacterial agents they are included here to emphasize that they may present in a similar way to a viral pneumonia. This must be borne in mind when examining a patient at the acute stage of the illness because the atypical pneumonias respond to antibiotic therapy. There may be a delay in achieving a specific laboratory diagnosis and it is critically important that the clinician should not (a) assume that it is a viral pneumonia and withhold treatment, or (b) treat with penicillins which are ineffective. A reasonable working rule in the case of a pneumonia which is not obviously due to pneumococcus or another defined organism, is to take samples for laboratory examination and then commence treatment with erythromycin to cover the possibility of a non-viral agent.

Further reading

Webster R. G., Laver W. G., Air G. M. *et al.* (1982) Molecular mechanisms of variation in influenza viruses. *Nature,* **296**, 115–121.

Stuart–Harris C. H., Schild G. C. (1976) *Influenza: The Viruses and the Disease.* Publishing Sciences Group, Littleton, Mass.

Baum S. G. (1979) Adenovirus. In: Mandell G. L., Douglas R. G., Bennett J. E. (eds) *Principles and Practice of Infectious Diseases.* John Wiley, New York.

Chanock R. M., Hyun W. K., Brandt C. *et al.* (1976).

Respiratory syncytial virus. In: Evans A. S. (ed.) *Viral Infections of Humans: Epidemiology and Control.* Plenum Publishing Co., New York.

Chapter 8
Childhood Fevers

The viral diseases described in this chapter (mumps, measles, rubella and erythema infectiosum) can, of course, be seen in people of all ages but they are more common in childhood. They share certain features:

1 They have a worldwide distribution with a high incidence of infection in non-immune individuals.

2 Transmission is primarily by the ororespiratory route.

3 As they are systemic infections they normally produce immunity to reinfection.

4 Humans appear to be the sole reservoir of infection.

Varicella could be reasonably included in this section but this manifestation of varicella-zoster infection is included with the other herpesviruses in Chapter 10.

Mumps

Mumps is a member of the Paramyxoviridae which exists in only one known serotype. The incubation period has a range of 12–29 days but, in most cases, disease develops after 16–18 days. The most common and obvious features are fever and tender enlargement of the salivary glands particularly the parotids. The parotitis may be unilateral or bilateral and persist for 7–10 days. Enlargement of the other salivary glands is not uncommon and there is usually associated tender cervical adenopathy. At the acute stage the patient often suffers from pain on jaw movement. Mumps virus shows a tropism for glandular tissue which accounts for some of the complications and it may also involve other tissues as is evident from some of the less common manifestations. Acute pancreatitis sometimes occurs at the acute stage and this should be suspected if the patient suffers acute abdominal pain and vomiting. The serum amylase levels are raised but in interpreting this finding it should be remembered that moderate elevations can result from retention of salivary amylase which may be absorbed from inflamed and blocked salivary ducts. Orchitis, which occurs in approximately 10% of post-pubertal males is a painful complication which often produces worries concerning future sterility; this outcome is rare. Invasion of the nervous sytem is quite common and the presence of virus in cerebrospinal fluid, together with a mild lymphocytosis, has been recorded in 30% of patients with uncomplicated mumps. Symptomatic meningitis, which is usually mild occurs in 10% of patients. Rarer effects of nervous system involvement are the development during the convalescent phase of a post infectious encephalomyelitis, transverse myelitis and polyneuritis (see Chapter 12). The following rare complications have been recorded: thyroiditis, mastitis, myocarditis, nephritis, arthritis, thrombocytopenic purpura and pneumonia.

As might be expected with a virus that is capable of producing disease in many different sites, viraemia is present at the acute stage and viruria is common. Most infections occur between the ages of 5 and 15 years and although most cases are apparent in late winter and spring they may present at any time. Asymptomatic attacks are common (30–40% of cases) and the transmission rate to susceptibles is approximately 85%. Patients may be infectious during the incubation period; virus is often present in the nasopharynx for seven days before until nine days after the illness.

Laboratory diagnosis

Mumps virus can be readily isolated from body fluids early in the illness. Saliva collected into a universal container, throat washings or swabs, urine and, when appropriate, cerebrospinal fluid provide good samples for isolation. The virus grows well in primary monkey kidney cells to produce syncytia and haemagglutinin and it may also be isolated in the allantoic cavity of embryonated hen's eggs. Complement fixation tests are useful for confirming the diagnosis and these may be important in the differential diagnosis of parotid swelling, abdominal pain and the other complications. Two antigen systems are normally used; the S (soluble) antigen which is derived from the nucleocapsid and the V (viral) antigen from the viral envelope. Antibodies to these antigens appear at different times after the appearance of symptoms and the pattern of responses can be used to date an infection. Antibodies to the S antigen rise within 3–5 days of the onset of illness and persist for 6–8 months while antibodies to the V antigen appear more slowly to reach a maximum at 2–4 weeks and then remain detectable for years. Other antibody detection sytems can be used to detect immunity to mumps including haemagglutination inhibition, neutralization and more recently radial haemolysis.

Prevention of infection

A live attenuated vaccine, produced in chick embryo cell cultures, is available to prevent mumps infection. This produces seroconversion in >95% of recipients and is known to be safe, potent and long lasting. It is currently being administered in combination with rubella and measles vaccine to children in the United States. There is no effective antiviral therapy for mumps.

Measles

Measles virus, which is also a member of the paramyxovirus family, exists as a single serotype. Two related viruses of animals, canine distemper virus and rinderpest virus of cattle, have not been associated with human infections. The incubation period ranges from 7–18 days (usually 9–11 days) and the first clinical effects are typical of a severe upper respiratory infection with fever, cough, coryzal symptoms and often conjunctivitis. Within the first three days of illness Koplik's spots may be seen on the buccal mucosa opposite the molar teeth. These appear as pinpoint greyish-white spots situated on an erythematous base and their presence is diagnostic. Within a day of the appearance of Koplik's spots the typical skin rash (exanthem) develops and this classically starts on the face in front of the ears and then spreads to the trunk and extremities. The rash is maculopapular, semiconfluent and velvety in nature and lasts for 3–5 days before fading. Generalized lymphadenopathy is usually present and the systemic symptoms subside as the rash begins to fade. Measles is likely to be particularly severe in the immunocompromised and in those suffering from malnutrition. In these individuals the respiratory symptoms are pronounced and often lead to pneumonia and severe diarrhoea. If T cell function is subnormal, and this is likely in malnutrition as well as in defined immunodeficiency states, the classical rash may not develop; involvement of the skin results in widespread desquamation and this atypical form of the disease is associated with a high mortality (often 15–25% in developing countries).

The commonest complications of measles are due to bacterial infection and these include otitis media, sinusitis, pneumonia and septicaemia. Involvement of the nervous system can be demonstrated by electroencephalography in up to 50% of uncomplicated cases and signs of post-infectious encephalitis occur 3–14 days after the acute illness in approximately 0.1% of patients. This is a potentially serious complication which carries a mortality in the region of 15% and neurological sequelae such as cranial nerve defects and mental retardation in approximately 25%. Haemorrhages may be present during the acute phase of measles due to thrombocytopenia. Exacerbation of quiescent tuberculosis, due to the immunosuppressive effects of the virus has been recorded. Viraemia is present at the acute stage and the virus may be demonstrated in T lymphocytes. This transient invasion of the the immune system results in a period of immunocompromise. The depression of cell-mediated immune mechanisms can be demonstrated by the fact that an individual who normally produces a skin reaction to tuberculin loses this responsiveness during, and immediately following, an attack of measles. Persistence of measles in the nervous system may lead to the late complication of subacute sclerosing panencephalitis. This disease is described in Chapter 12.

In the respiratory tract, measles virus produces necrosis of the mucosa and inflammatory changes similar to those caused by other respiratory tract viruses. In the skin, the areas involved in the exanthem show a vasculitis characterized by vascular dilatation, oedema and perivascular mononuclear cell infiltrates. There is hyperplasia of lymphoid tissue and the presence in the lymph nodes, respiratory tract epithelium and urinary sediment, of large multinucleated giant cells (Warthin-Finkeldey cells) which often contain intranuclear and intracytoplasmic inclusions.

Specific immune responses, which develop during the course of the infection limit disease development and lead to lifelong protection against reinfection. Humoral antibodies become detectable in the first few days, reach maximum levels at 2–3 weeks after the onset of symptoms, and persist at a low level for life.

In communities with a low level of vaccine-induced immunity most cases of measles occur in children after the age of six months (due to the protective effect of maternal IgG). Where the acceptance rate for immunization of children is high, the reduced risk of exposure to the wild virus means that there is an increased risk of infection to susceptibles in the older age groups. Epidemics of measles occur in the winter and spring in 1–3 year cycles. Widespread immunization has been shown to delay the appearance of an epidemic due to the reduction in the pool of susceptibles. Asymptomatic infections are uncommon (<5% of cases) and the virus spreads readily to susceptibles in households or institutions with a transmission rate of approximately 85%. The period of communicability is estimated to be from four days before the appearance of the rash until five days after.

In view of the respiratory tract involvement during the prodrome it is likely that individuals are most infectious at this early stage.

Laboratory diagnosis

Most cases of measles can be diagnosed without difficulty by clinical examination with particular emphasis on the observation of Koplik's spots and the distribution and nature of the rash. In atypical cases laboratory diagnosis is important and may be achieved by several methods. Immunofluorescence applied to desquamated cells from the oropharynx or urinary sediment provides a rapid method and this may be used to confirm the suspicion raised by the finding of multinucleated giant cells. The virus may be isolated from the oropharynx and urine during the first five days of the illness and its growth, in primary monkey kidney cells, can be detected by giant cell formation. Retrospective diagnosis can be achieved by demonstration of seroconversion using complement fixation, haemagglutination inhibition, neutralization or immunofluorescence tests. Radial haemolysis may be employed as a screening test to detect immunity from past infection.

Prevention of infection

Live, attenuated vaccine is available. This is highly immunogenic and has a very low complication rate. Immunization is recommended for children after the first year of life and normally at 13–15 months. This is the optimal time to avoid the risks of exposure to wild virus which increase as the child comes into contact with other children and the immune system responds well at this age. Immunization in the first year is less satisfactory probably due to the residual protection from maternal IgG together with immaturity of the baby's immune system. The vaccine must not be given to anyone with known or suspected immunocompromise. Immunization of patients in long term remission from treated acute lymphoblastic leukaemia has resulted in a subacute encephalopathy. A similar contraindication applies to women in pregnancy. Post-exposure prophylaxis can be successfully achieved by intramuscular injection of human normal immunoglobulin (HNIG). As indicated in Chapter 5, this is obtained from routine donors and is highly effective in preventing or attenuating an attack of measles provided it is administered within six days of exposure. Passive prophylaxis of this type provides short term protection and, in those for whom vaccine is contraindicated, this may be necessary repeatedly throughout life.

There is no specific antiviral treatment for measles virus infection.

Rubella

Rubella (German measles) is caused by an enveloped RNA virus which is classified as a togavirus. Only one serotype is known to exist and there is no evidence of infection in non-human hosts. Rubella infection in children and adults is almost always mild and uneventful and it would be of only passing interest except for the most serious implications of transplacental infection of the fetus. These aspects of rubella are described in Chapter 15.

The incubation period is usually 14–16 days (range 14–21 days). Following a short prodromal illness (usually one day) comprising a low-grade fever, pharyngitis and often mild conjunctivitis associated with cervical, post auricular and occipital lymphadenopathy, the characteristic maculopapular rash appears which is most prominent on the head and trunk. The rash is much finer and less obvious than that of measles, does not cause a palpable infiltration of the skin and does not show the same tendency to become confluent. It rarely lasts for more than three days and often fluctuates in intensity. It must be emphasized that it is impossible to make a firm diagnosis of rubella infection on the basis of these clinical manifestations; other viruses particularly echoviruses and parvovirus can produce similar effects and the rubella rash can be mimicked by mild drug eruptions. It is important to remember this when interpreting the possible significance of rashes in pregnancy or in those who have been in contact with pregnant women. The only certain way of confirming the diagnosis and counselling the patient is to carry out serological tests (see Chapter 15). It should also be remembered that rubella is often asymptomatic. Despite the absence of symptoms, the fetus is still at risk of infection from viraemia in the mother. Thus any knowledge of exposure to possible rubella during pregnancy should be taken seriously, regardless of the state of health of the woman, and laboratory investigations should be initiated.

The commonest complication of rubella is arthralgia and this may progress to an arthritis involving particularly the finger and wrist joints but also occasionally the elbows, knees and ankles. This appears to be commoner in women and is associated with a delay in elimination of the virus and persistence of rubella-specific IgM. Although it may on occasion raise the suspicion of early rheumatoid arthritis, rubella arthritis is short-lived and rarely lasts for more than three months. Thrombocytopenia is a very common sequel to acute rubella (and to rubella immunization) but very rarely results in bleeding or purpura. The transient fall in circulating platelets is thought to result from their binding to the Fc fragment of rubella IgG combined with haemagglutinin. These circulating complexes are removed from circulation by phagocytes at a rate which is faster than platelet release from megakaryocytes. Rubella is a rare cause of post-infectious encephalomyelitis.

Viraemia is present for approximately seven days before the onset of the rash and, as illustrated in Chapter 4, the association of the rash with the rapid rise in haemagglutination inhibiting antibodies and the cessation of viraemia suggests that the illness is immunopathological. Antibodies reach a maximum within two weeks and remain detectable for life. Re-exposure to the virus usually results in a rapid stimulation of specific IgG but the evidence for significant viraemia or threat to the fetus is very limited.

Infections are commoner during the winter and spring months but the virus is much less easily transmitted between children and adults than measles virus. This means that before the vaccine became widely available, 10–15% of adults escaped infection during childhood. This figure defined the population of women of child-bearing age who were vulnerable to exposure during early pregnancy. The problem of rubella in pregnancy still persists in the United Kingdom due to inadequate acceptance or provision of the vaccine.

A neonate with congenital rubella presents a quite different risk to the non-immune. Because of the high levels of virus excretion in the nasopharynx of these babies, an infectious dose is much more easily transmitted than from older children with postnatal rubella. The rubella baby, therefore, presents a considerable threat to women in pregnancy who are non-immune.

In postnatal rubella, the presence of virus in the nasopharynx for seven days before until seven days after the onset of the rash indicates the theoretical period during which the disease should be considered to be communicable.

Laboratory diagnosis

The virus may be isolated from respiratory secretions of children and adults at the acute stage of the illness. Cytopathic effects may be observed in continuous rabbit kidney lines (RK13) and silent growth in other cells can be detected by immunofluorescence. In congenitally infected neonates, the virus may also be isolated from tissues, faeces and urine. Virus isolation is often prolonged and unreliable particularly as the RK13 cells are inclined to lose sensitivity to rubella on serial passage.

Serological diagnosis is highly reliable and much more suitable for most diagnostic situations. Because of the importance of serology in the diagnosis of rubella in pregnancy, the details are described in Chapter 15.

Prevention of infection

Rubella vaccines have been available since 1969. The current vaccine (RA27/3) is a live attenuated strain grown in human diploid fibroblastic cells. It is potent, producing antibody levels comparable to those of the wild virus and is relatively free from side effects. Seroconversion occurs in more than 95% of recipients after a single dose. Although live vaccine virus may be detected in the nasopharynx following subcutaneous injection, the titre is lower than that found in wild rubella infection and it has never been shown to be transmissible. Immunization schedules vary in different countries. In the United Kingdom vaccine is offered to girls between the ages of 11 and 14; in the United States it is given to all infants after the first year of life. Both approaches are supplemented by antibody testing and immunization of susceptible women of childbearing age. The vaccine is contraindicated in the immunocompromised and in pregnancy. Pregnancy should be avoided for three months after vaccination as, although the risks to the fetus appear much less than with the wild virus, there are insufficient data to be certain of its safety. The duration of protection afforded by the vaccine is not known, but follow-up studies suggest that it is likely to cover the childbearing years. Trials of human normal immunoglobulin (HNIG) in pregnant women exposed to rubella have been unsuccessful. HNIG is likely to prevent the symptoms of rubella in the woman but does not prevent infection and abnormality in the fetus.

No specific antiviral compounds are available.

Erythema infectiosum (fifth disease)

Erythema infectiosum has been recognized for many years as a mild self-limiting disease seen mainly in school children. In 1983 the causative agent was identified as a parvovirus. The disease often occurs in outbreaks and the first sign of illness is marked erythema of the cheeks; this has been termed a 'slapped cheek' appearance. The rash then extends to the trunk and limbs and fades from the centre of the lesions to yield a reticular, lacy appearance. The rash lasts 1–2 weeks but may recur due to sunlight, exercise or stress. Fever and malaise are mild or absent but arthralgia is present in 80% of cases in adults and this may be the sole presenting feature. Infection during pregnancy has recently been associated with an increased risk of intrauterine death.

Experimental inoculation of volunteers has shown human parvovirus to be transmissible by the respiratory route and to produce a biphasic illness. One week after inoculation, in association with an intense plasma viraemia and infectious virus in the nasopharynx, there may be mild constitutional symptoms (fever, malaise, myalgia and headache). This prodromal illness is then followed by apparent recovery but blood counts reveal pancytopenia with a slight fall in haemoglobin concentration. At 17–18 days after inoculation the skin rash appears together with arthralgia and mild arthritis.

The infection may be more serious in individuals with chronic haemolytic anaemia such as sickle cell disease or hereditary spherocytosis. The reticulocytopenia caused by the transient bone marrow involvement may lead to an aplastic crisis and a marked fall in haemoglobin concentration. This complication may produce the need for blood transfusion.

Laboratory diagnosis

Human parvovirus infection can be diagnosed at an early stage by demonstration of virus in serum. No culture system is available at present and diagnosis rests on the demonstration of viral particles, by electron microscopy, or particle-associated DNA by the use of hybridization probes (dot-blotting). At the time of the rash, viraemia is not usually detectable and the infection may be confirmed by the demonstration of virus-specific IgM. This antibody remains detectable for approximately two months after infection.

Prevention of infection

No vaccines and no specific therapy are available. Isolation of individuals with rashes is not appropriate as, at this stage, they are no longer infectious.

Further reading

Feigin R. D. and Cherry J. D. (1981) *Textbook of Paediatric Infectious Disease*. W. B. Saunders, Philadelphia.

Krugman S., Ward R. and Katz S. L. (1977) *Infectious Diseases of Children*. C. V. Mosby, St Louis.

Chapter 9
Herpesviruses 1—Herpes Simplex

The two human herpes simplex viruses (HSV-1 and HSV-2) are members of the Herpesvirus group of the family Herpetiviridae. This group also includes cytomegalovirus (CMV), varicella-zoster virus (VZV) and Epstein-Barr virus (EBV). Herpesviruses produce a wide range of infections and the effects range from asymptomatic infections to life threatening diseases. They all produce latent infections. This means that, following primary infection, the viruses persist in a non-infectious state for the life of the individual. They retain the capacity to reactivate periodically with the return of infectivity which may be accompanied by disease. HSV can replicate in many different animal and human cells in culture but both types are exclusively human pathogens in nature. HSV1 and HSV2 are sufficiently different to be classed as separate viruses. They show approximately 50% base-sequence homology which is much greater than that shown between HSV and the other human herpesviruses. This difference in their genomic structure confers distinct epidemiologic and antigenic characteristics. The differences in their DNA are revealed by restriction endonuclease analysis (Fig. 9.1) and they can be distinguished biologically by their growth on the chorioallantoic membrane of the fertile hen's egg (chapter 6). There is, however, sharing of several antigens including surface glycoproteins and other structural polypeptides.

Pathogenesis

Herpes simplex viruses are transmitted through contact with infected lesions or secretions. The incubation period is 3–14 days. In those with normal immunity, lesions are mainly confined to tissues of ectodermal origin (skin, mouth, vagina, conjunctiva and central nervous system) but widespread dissemination may be seen in the immunocompromised. The two viruses show differences in the pattern of infection and disease potential. HSV-1 is mainly associated with oral infections and lesions above the waist. HSV-2 is predominantly a cause of disease in the genital tract and surrounding area. In most studies of initial episodes of genital herpes approximately 10–20% of isolates have been type 1.

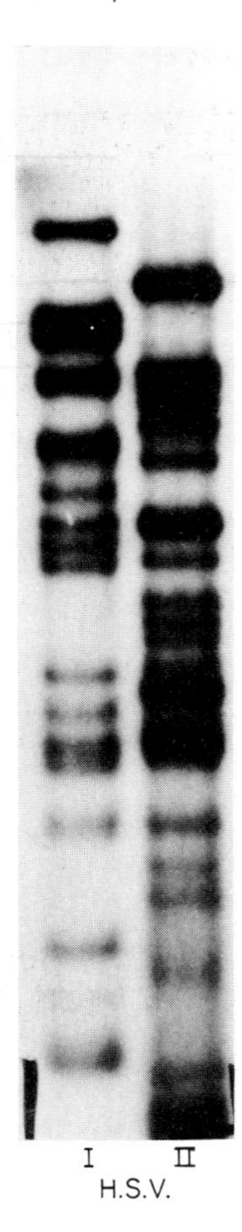

Fig. 9.1 Photograph of an autoradiograph of restriction endonuclease maps of herpes simplex virus types 1 and 2. Note the different banding patterns which can be used to distinguish these two viruses.

The characteristic early lesions produced by HSV are thin walled vesicles containing clear fluid with an underlying erythema produced by an inflammatory response. These soon rupture to produce shallow ulcers which, because of their superficial nature, do not normally scar. The floor of the ulcer crater contains exposed nerve endings and at this stage the lesions are painful. Over a period of several days, the ulcer heals by scabbing. The sequence of events in a skin vesicle is illustrated in Fig. 9.2. The virus may reach the basal layers of the epidermis by direct implantation into the skin, by transmission along

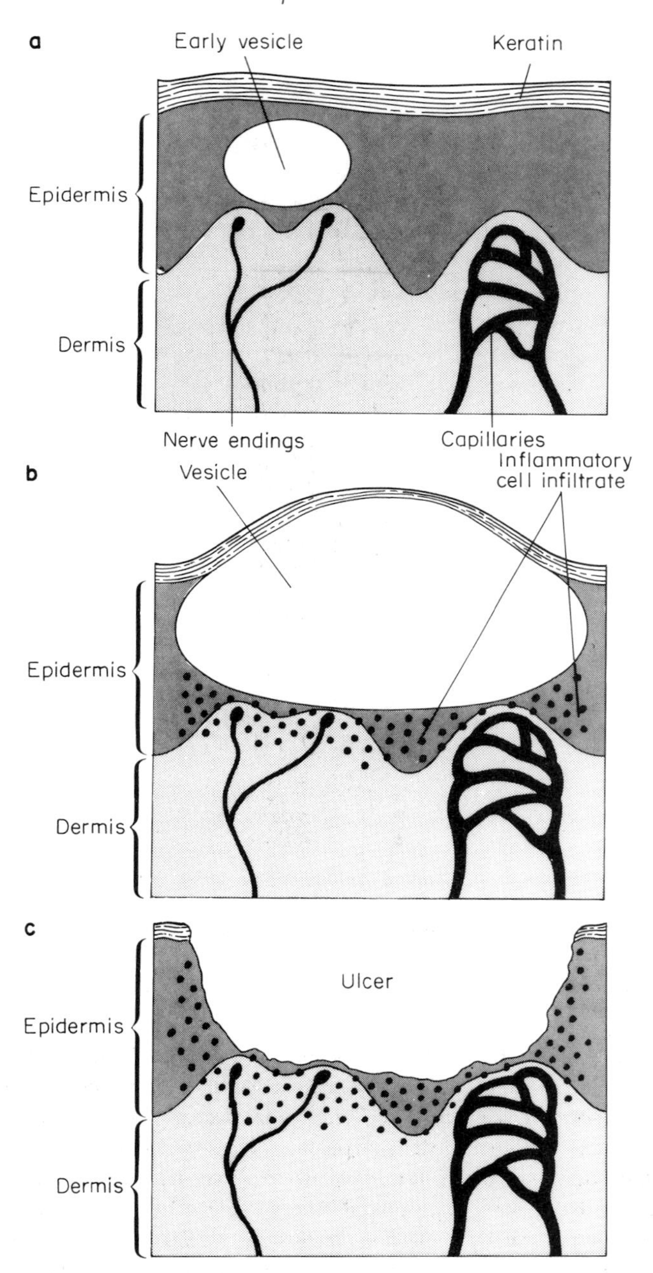

Fig. 9.2 Schematic illustration of the development of a typical skin vesicle caused by herpes simplex and varicella-zoster viruses.

nerve fibres or via the blood capillaries. Histological examination of lesions shows the development of multinucleated giant cells, ballooning degeneration of epithelial cells, focal necrosis and eosinophilic inclusion bodies. The inflammatory reaction involves, at first, mainly polymorphonuclear neutrophils and later infiltration with macrophages and lymphocytes. During primary infection the viruses may be detectable in circulation and, either by this route, or by neuronal spread (or both) establish a latent infection in sensory and autonomic nervous ganglia. Evidence that HSV-1 is latent in the trigeminal ganglia has accumulated as a result of surgical procedures used to abolish trigeminal neuralgia. Section of the nerve root (Fig. 9.3, point A) usually results in cold sore development in those who are infected with the virus. When the nerve is severed peripheral to the ganglion (point B), or if the ganglion is destroyed by alcohol or coagulation (point C) , the virus does not cause lip lesions and the procedure usually prevents future cold sore formation. Careful examination of skin in the lip region failed to reveal virus or viral antigen except at times of recurrences of cold sores and if skin was transplanted from an area normally affected recurrences were observed at the usual site and not on the region of the graft.

In recent years, latent HSV-1 has been demonstrated in the trigeminal, superior cervical and vagal ganglia by co-cultivation techniques and restriction endonuclease analysis has revealed that most

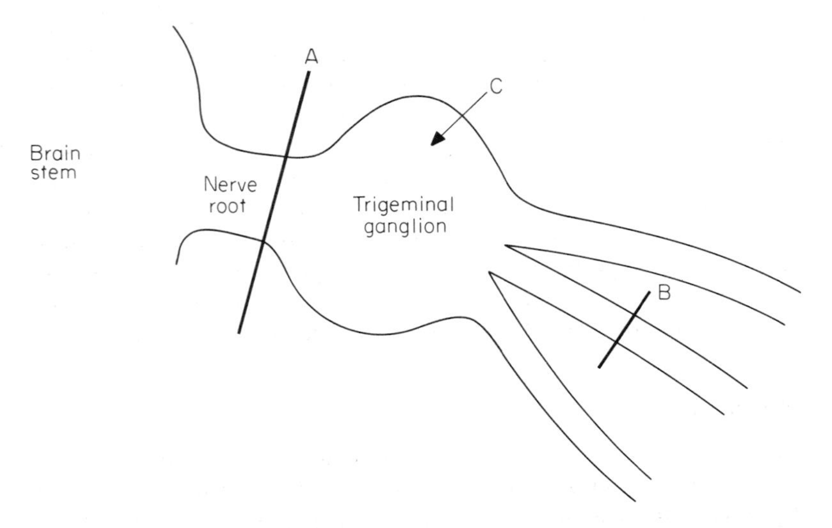

Fig. 9.3 Diagram of trigeminal ganglion showing the points A–C favoured in attempts to relieve neuralgia by surgical intervention (see text).

individuals have only one strain of latent virus within the nervous system. Latent HSV-2 has been isolated by similar methods from dorsal root ganglia in the sacral (S2–S3) region. The exact mechanism of latency within the cells of nerve ganglia is unknown but the evidence points more towards persistence of viral genome in episomal form rather than a steady-state infection restrained by immune responses. Reactivation of latent HSV-1 occurs as a result of several defined stimuli: fever, stress and menstruation are common triggers. In addition to these, increased exposure to ultra-violet light (often experienced during skiing holidays) is likely to precipitate an attack. In animal models latent virus can be activated by mild skin trauma. After triggering the virus travels down peripheral nerves to the skin where it replicates in epidermal cells. During this phase of neuronal transfer the individual often experiences minor sensory disturbances (usually paraesthesiae) in the affected area. The triggers for HSV-2 are less clearly defined, but most sufferers attribute recurrences either to stress or recent sexual intercourse.

Immunology

Host factors appear to be very important in governing the pattern of disease in an individual. Many people infected with HSV-1 never experience a cold sore. Disease caused by primary infections is usually more severe and prolonged than that of recurrences due to the time taken to mount an effective immune response. Infection with one type of HSV does not protect against subsequent infection with the other type. There is, however, some evidence that previous infection with HSV-1 shortens the duration and severity of primary HSV-2. Herpes simplex spreads by cell to cell transfer and for this reason, although high levels of neutralizing antibody are produced, cell-mediated immunity is thought to be the major means of controlling infections. This is supported by the fact that, while herpes infections cause no major problems to those with hypogammaglobulinaemia, severe and persistent infections often leading to viraemic dissemination are frequently seen in patients with deficient cellular immunity.

Epidemiology

Infection with HSV-1 usually occurs in children during the first five years. The prevalence of infection as judged by antibody presence depends on the socioeconomic status of the population. In the United Kingdom most studies show that 60–70% of adults have been infected but the prevalence usually exceeds 90% in developing countries. HSV-2 is virtually always a sexually transmitted infection and antibody is rarely found in children or in chaste populations. Antibody studies show that most infections occur, as with other sexually transmitted diseases, during early adult life.

Diseases caused by herpes simplex viruses

1. *Gingivostomatitis*

Approximately 10% of primary infections with HSV-1 produce gingivostomatitis; the majority of childhood infections are asymptomatic. Vesicles develop on the tongue, gums,buccal mucosa and pharynx and these rupture to form painful ulcers. The child is usually febrile, irritable and refusing to eat and the illness resolves uneventfully in 5–10 days. During the primary infection, symptomatic or not, the virus enters its latent state in nerve ganglia. Primary oral infection in adults may present with pharyngitis which is often accompanied by a prominent exudate. This is often caused by HSV-2 and may result from oro-genital contact.

2. *Cold sores*

Recurrent lesions (cold sores) result from reactivation from the trigeminal ganglia and usually produce minor local disease with no systemic effects. Less than half of those infected with HSV-1 experience cold sores and regular sufferers can usually detect an impending lesion by paraesthesiae in the affected region. The lesions are usually unilateral and situated on the lip-margin or perioral area. Repeated recurrences occur in the same region. The typical sequence of erythema leading to vesicle formation, ulceration, scabbing and healing is more rapidly followed than in primary gingivostomatitis. Healing is normally complete in seven days. Asymptomatic reactivation of HSV-1 is common. Virus has been isolated from the saliva of 2–5% of randomly screened adults and the virus was present in 27% on repeated sampling from HSV antibody positive individuals.

3. *Skin infections*

Herpes simplex of either type may be implanted in the skin and lead to a painful primary lesion. Infection of the fingers, herpetic whitlow, is an occupational hazard of health-care workers and results from penetration of the skin by a bite or infected sharp instrument or by contamination of an abrasion with virus. Painful vesicles develop into an ulcerated area and there is usually regional lymphadenopathy. Primary skin infection is associated with wrestling (herpes gladiatorum) and facial contact between rugby forwards in the scrum, a condition known as 'scrum-pox'. Recurrent disease may result from these skin infections and subsequent attacks are usually in the same region.

4

Eye disease

Herpes simplex is the commonest infectious cause of blindness in developed countries. Transfer of virus to the eye may result in conjunctivitis and corneal ulceration. Classical dendritic ulcers or punctate ulceration can be highlighted by fluorescein. Recurrences in the eye are likely to be more damaging than the primary disease as the infection often penetrates into the deeper structures. The tragic complication of pan-orbital ulceration may develop very rapidly if steroid drops, which cause local immunosuppression, are used.

5

Genital herpes

Primary genital herpes is caused by HSV-1 and HSV-2 although the former is much less likely to produce recurrences. The degree of severity is variable but pain and discomfort are often marked and the lesions may be present for 10–14 days. The patient develops patches of vesicles in the genital area and these soon turn to extremely painful ulcers. There is usually itching and vaginal or urethral discharge and, in the acute phase, fever, malaise, headache and myalgia commonly occur. Acute retention of urine is occasionally seen and, as urinary problems may persist for some days after the lesions have healed, this probably reflects involvement of the vesical nerves with the virus. Genital herpes is more likely to be recurrent than buccal herpes but, as with cold sores, reactivation usually results in mild disease of shorter duration than the primary attack. The frequency of recurrence, which varies in different people, seems to decrease with age.

6

Neonatal herpes

The neonate, particularly if premature, is ill equipped to cope with HSV. This results from immaturity of the immune system and specifically macrophages. Infection usually results from contact with infected genital secretions from the mother during birth although the viruses may also be transmitted from cold sores present in the father or attending staff. Retrospective investigations of women who have produced babies with neonatal herpes usually fail to reveal a history of genital lesions or contact with an infected partner. This supports the view that the neonate is most likely to become infected from a primary infection occurring just before term. In this situation the baby may not be protected by transplacental IgG. Neonatal disease is of varying severity but if the virus disseminates to internal organs the mortality, if untreated, approaches 100%. Pneumonia, hepatitis, adrenal necrosis and widespread encephalitis are common manifestations of viraemic spread and these serious effects may occur in the absence of skin lesions.

Nervous system disease

Aseptic meningitis is a rare complication of genital herpes. The virus can be isolated from cerebrospinal fluid and this usually benign disease normally resolves without sequelae.

Herpes simplex encephalitis (see Chapter 12) is a most serious infection at any age. In the neonate, viraemic spread of infection leads to extensive brain destruction while in older children and adults the lesions are usually more localized. Most cases occur in those who have high levels of HSV antibody which suggests that virus reactivated in the trigeminal ganglion has ascended to the brain. This may explain the frequent localization of lytic lesions to the temporo-parietal areas. The growth of virus in brain tissue leads to acute inflammation and associated oedema and this process is likely to produce focal neurological signs, progressive coma and the danger of death from coning. The mortality is 70% in the absence of treatment and there is a high risk of neurological sequelae in those who survive.

The compromised host

Eczema predisposes to the dissemination of HSV. This is most likely to occur in active eczematous lesions but it may also complicate infections in those individuals with atopy whose skin condition is quiescent. Herpes simplex is an important opportunist pathogen in patients with deficient cell-mediated immunity in whom infection is usually endogenous and arising from reactivation of latent virus. The increased use of immunosuppressive drugs for transplantation procedures, together with the appearance of the acquired immune deficiency syndrome (AIDS), has led to increasing numbers of HSV infections in the immunocompromised. A local lesion, which would normally be minor and short-lived, is likely to be severe and prolonged in the immunocompromised. Unless treatment is promptly applied the virus may be locally invasive and may also enter the circulation to produce disseminated lesions.

Laboratory diagnosis

Virus isolation is the best way of diagnosing infection with HSV. Although many cell culture systems may be used, most laboratories use human embryo fibroblasts. The characteristic focal lesions are usually evident within 24–72 hours of inoculation (Chapter 6). The isolates can be typed by immunofluorescence using specific monoclonal antibodies or by restriction endonuclease analysis. Direct examination of clinical material by electron microscopy may reveal herpes particles and, although this will not distinguish HSV from other members of the group, it may be important in achieving a diagnosis. Immunofluorescence applied directly to scrapings from lesions or tissue sections, while less sensitive than culture, may give a more rapid diagnosis. Serological methods can be used to demonstrate primary infections but recurrences do not usually produce alterations in antibody titres.

Prevention

Prototype vaccines have been developed but their efficacy has not yet been evaluated. Avoidance of contact with infected secretions is the only possible approach to avoiding infection although, as asymptomatic shedding is known to occur, this is not always possible. Condoms have been shown to exclude HSV-2 in experimental systems and their use is recommended if active genital lesions are present. Most obstetricians favour caesarian section if visible genital lesions are present at term and sensible infection control measures should be enforced to avoid dissemination of virus in neonatal units and in wards accommodating the immunocompromised.

Treatment

The treatment of choice for HSV in any site is acyclovir (see Chapter

6). Many trials of this drug, which is available in oral, topical and intravenous formulations, have shown it to be a potent and safe preparation which will rapidly eliminate virus replication in those with normal or compromised host responses. In addition to this, acyclovir can be given prophylactically to those who are particularly vulnerable (e.g. bone marrow transplant recipients) in order to suppress infection. It must be emphasized, however, that no drug has been found which will influence the virus in its latent state or prevent its reactivation. Although the introduction of acyclovir has removed the need to use the older, more toxic drugs for systemic therapy some alternatives such as idoxuridine, vidarabine and trifluorothymidine still have a place in the topical therapy of corneal HSV.

Further reading

Hill T. J. (1983) Herpes simplex latency. In: *The Herpesviruses*, Roizman B. (Ed). Plenum Press, New York.

Nahmias A. J., Dowdle W. R. and Schinazi R. F. (1981) *The Human Herpesviruses*. Elsevier, New York.

Roizman B. (1982) The family herpesviridae—general description, taxonomy and classification. In: *The Herpesviruses*, Roizman B. (ed). Plenum Press, New York.

Chapter 10
Herpesviruses 2—VZV, CMV, EBV

Varicella-zoster virus (VZV)

Varicella (chickenpox) and zoster (shingles) are two diseases which are caused by the same virus (VZV). The virus is morphologically identical to herpes simplex viruses. Varicella is the acute disease which follows primary infection and zoster results from reactivation of the virus which has remained in a latent state in sensory nerve ganglia. Varicella is a generalized infection which is characterized by a vesicular eruption of the skin and mucous membranes. Zoster is involvement of one or more dermatomes with pain, resulting from inflammation of the posterior nerve roots and ganglia, followed by crops of vesicles in the skin supplied by those sensory nerves. Because of its dermatomal localization zoster is almost always unilateral.

Pathogenesis

Varicella is transmitted by aerosols and the primary site of infection is probably the mucosa of the upper respiratory tract. The early illness is characterized by bouts of fever and each febrile episode is accompanied by a release of virus into the circulation. These successive viraemias lead to deposition of virus in skin capillaries and epidermal replication of the virus results in skin vesicles which are very similar to those of herpes simplex (see Chapter 9). The intermittent nature of the dissemination of virus initiates vesicles at different times and this accounts for the characteristic skin rash of varicella; superficial vesicles, pustules and ulcers all present at the same time. This is in contrast to the exanthema of variola and monkeypox (see Chapter 17) in which, as a result of a single episode of viraemia, all lesions are at the same stage of development. During varicella the virus enters and establishes a state of latency in dorsal root and cranial nerve ganglia. As with herpes simplex viruses, the presence of latent virus in ganglionic material has been demonstrated by DNA hybridization studies, but the nature of the virus or its DNA in the tissue is unknown.

Reactivation of the virus can occur at any time in life but its increased frequency in the elderly suggests that immune mechanisms, which are known to be less competent in later life, have a part to play in maintaining the latent state. This is further supported by the fact that zoster is commoner in those who are significantly immunocompromised due to malignancy or chemotherapy. Approximately 50% of the population develop zoster at some time and, although it is normally associated with ageing, it is occasionally seen in young children. The triggers which lead to viral reactivation are not as clearly defined as with herpes simplex but there appears to be a significant association between trigeminal nerve zoster and chronic sinusitis. In patients with zoster in other regions, investigators have attributed the cause to arthritic changes involving the nerve roots associated with the dermatomes involved. Although zoster may be recurrent in the immunocompromised, it is rare for it to recur in those with normal immune responses. Post mortem studies of individuals with zoster who have died for other reasons have revealed acute inflammatory changes and necrosis in the affected ganglia and extending along the sensory nerves to the skin. The absence of any inflammation central to the sensory ganglia is further evidence for latency in those sites.

Immunology

Humoral and cell-mediated immunity are important in VZV infections. Circulating antibody prevents reinfection and cell-mediated mechanisms appear to control reactivation and prevent dissemination of dermatomal lesions.

Epidemiology

Varicella infection is ubiquitous and approximately 90% of cases occur in children before the age of 10 years. Man is the only known host and the virus is highly contagious with transmission rates to susceptibles in the region of 75%. Infection is most frequent during the winter and spring and it may be acquired from contact with either varicella or zoster infection. Infectivity in varicella is maximal for 24–48 hours before the onset of the rash and lasts for 3–4 days after its appearance. Zoster is sporadic and occurs throughout the year. The period of infectivity is more prolonged than in varicella as vesicle formation extends gradually along a dermatome and, therefore, replicating virus is present for longer.

Clinical effects

The incubation period for varicella is 14–21 days and the onset of the illness is usually heralded by malaise and fever which are followed after a few hours by the rash. The vesicles appear first on the trunk and soon spread to the face and the limbs. They are very thin walled, irregular in shape and, typically of herpes vesicles, have an underlying area of erythema which indicates an inflammatory response to the presence of replicating virus in the epidermis. The distribution of the rash is described as centripetal (i.e. more concentrated centrally than peripherally on the body surface) in contrast to the centrifugal rash of variola. Inspection of the mouth soon after the rash has appeared may reveal the presence of vesicles or ulcers on the tongue, buccal mucosa and fauces and these are heavily infected with virus. It is at this stage that the patient is likely to be most infectious from airborne dissemination. As described above, the vesicles increase in number with each episode of fever and all stages of lesion development are present once the rash has fully appeared. The superficial site of viral replication in the skin (basal layers of the epidermis) means that, unless the lesions become secondarily infected with bacteria, they normally heal without scarring. The rash is pruritic (itchy) and the tendency for the patient to scratch may lead to bacterial superinfection. Generalized lymphadenopathy develops at the time of the prodromal illness and becomes maximal during the period of the rash. When the last vesicles have appeared, the fever subsides and full recovery is normal within a few days.

Complications are unusual in the normally immune; varicella pneumonia (which may lead to asymptomatic calcified lesions visible radiologically) and post-infectious encephalomyelitis are the most serious. Varicella occurring in individuals with deficient cell-mediated immunity may be severe and life-threatening. Prolonged viraemia may be associated with intense vesicle formation (with haemorrhagic lesions) and visceral dissemination leading to pneumonia, encephalitis, hepatitis and nephritis. A neonate infected from a mother who develops varicella at, or just before term, is unprotected by maternal IgG and, because of its immature immune system, is likely to develop severe, disseminated disease similar to that seen in congenital or acquired cellular immune deficiency.

The onset of zoster is usually heralded by pain in the region of the affected dermatome and this may be attributed to arthritis or neuralgia until the diagnosis becomes apparent with the appearance of the rash. The interval between the development of pain and vesicle formation may be several days. The rash normally involves 1–3 dermatomes and, over a period of several days, successive crops of vesicles appear over the sensory nerve distribution. Approximately 10% of cases have involvement of the trigeminal nerve and this presentation may lead to facial disfiguration and eye damage. Zoster in the elderly is often followed by persistent postherpetic neuralgia. This severe and persistent pain is localized to the dermatomes involved in the initiating zoster and it can be extremely difficult to control even with the most powerful analgesics. It is occasionally necessary to consider neurosurgical intervention, either to section the affected nerves or ablate the ganglia, in some cases of post-herpetic neuralgia.

Immunocompromised patients who develop zoster may be unable to localize the virus within the skin and entry into the circulation may lead to disseminated zoster.

Laboratory diagnosis

Electron microscopy provides a useful means of approaching the differential diagnosis of a vesicular eruption. Vesicle fluid examined by negative staining may contain recognizable herpesvirus particles and, although it is not possible to distinguish VZV from other herpesviruses, this information when taken with the clinical details may be all that is necessary to make a presumptive diagnosis and if necessary commence specific therapy. The technique was of considerable value in the past in distinguishing between the rashes of varicella and variola (smallpox). Direct examination of material from the base of vesicles may provide a means of rapid diagnosis. Histological staining may reveal the presence of multinucleated giant cells and intranuclear inclusions may be present. A more specific approach to diagnosis is the use of immunofluorescence on cells from the lesions. Virus may be isolated in human embryo fibroblasts and a focal CPE is normally seen in 3–7 days. The isolation may be confirmed by immunofluorescence or neutralization. The virus does not replicate in laboratory animals or embryonated eggs and orthopoxviruses and herpes simplex viruses, both of which produce pocks on the chorioallantoic membrane, can be distinguished from VZV in this way. Serological diagnosis may be obtained by complement fixation tests, neutralization, immunofluorescence or ELISA. IgM antibody tests have been adapted from these methods and detection of IgM can be used to indicate recent activity of the virus. Varicella is followed by seroconversion with a classical primary immune response. Zoster can occur in the presence of high levels of neutralizing antibody, but when the virus re-emerges after many decades there is frequently a second IgM response in conjunction with a boosting of pre-existing IgG levels.

Prevention and treatment

Zoster immune globulin (ZIG) is prepared from donors who have recently convalesced from varicella or zoster. It is limited in availability and should only be considered for protection of individuals, exposed to the virus, whose life would be threatened if they were to acquire the infection. Immunocompromised children, such as those with leukaemia, and neonates exposed to the virus from maternal infection around the time of delivery are groups in whom this approach is normally adopted. A live, attenuated varicella virus vaccine is currently under evaluation but has not yet come into general use.

The antiviral agent acyclovir has been shown, in extensive clinical trials, to be active against VZV although higher blood levels (and therefore higher doses) are required than for herpes simplex infections. This drug should be offered to all patients with evidence of significant immunocompromise at the first signs of varicella or zoster. Varicella in normally immune people does not usually require antiviral therapy but if the condition is severe, and particularly if the rash is haemorrhagic or a severe pneumonia develops, the drug should be given immediately. Normally immune people with uncomplicated zoster should be considered for acyclovir therapy but in view of the fact that patients often report too late for the drug to be effective, together with the cost involved in using the drug, it will probably be reserved for severe cases and particularly those with trigeminal nerve involvement.

Patients presenting with varicella or zoster may become secondarily infected with bacteria and these infections may require appropriate antibiotic therapy. In addition to this, provision of antipruritic drugs (e.g. antihistamines) during the acute stage of varicella may not only lead to more comfort for the patient but may also contribute to preventing bacterial invasion by removing the desire to scratch the skin.

Cytomegalovirus (CMV)

Human cytomegalovirus acquired its name as a result of the histological appearance of infected cells. These are large cells (25–40 μm diameter) which contain a large intranuclear inclusion. This inclusion displaces the chromatin and the nuclear membrane is swollen and prominent; this morphology has led to the term 'owl-eye cells' (Chapter 6). Cytomegalic cells were originally observed by histologists in three types of situation:

1 They were occasionally widely disseminated in patients with malignant disease, particularly if they had received immunosuppressive therapy.

2 Similar widespread histological changes were found, as a very rare event, in the neonate; these were associated with certain congenital abnormalities and the condition became known as cytomegalic inclusion disease.

3 They were commonly identified in the salivary glands of children who had suffered traumatic or other unconnected deaths; this infection was asymptomatic and CMV was known as the salivary gland virus.

CMV has the largest genome of all the herpes viruses but it is morphologically indistinguishable from the other members.

Pathogenesis

CMV is a virus of very low cytocidal capacity in the host with normal immune responses and, although it establishes persistent infections in the salivary glands of children and occasionally the cervix and renal tubular epithelium, it seems to cause no functional disturbance in these sites. After primary infection it becomes latent in leucocytes and, although the nature and extent of incorporation in each of the cellular elements is unknown, the frequency of transmission from granulocyte transfusions indicates that these cells are important for persistence of the virus. In pregnancy, the virus may be transmitted through the placenta and disseminated infection of the fetus may lead to congenital abnormality. Children or adults with deficient cell-mediated immunity may suffer disease in a variety of tissues as a result of viraemic spread and widespread replication of the virus.

Immunology

It is not known whether infection with CMV in the normally immune confers solid protection against reinfection with another strain of the virus. In the immunocompromised infection with different strains has been described and this may be related to low levels of circulating antibody. As with the other herpesviruses, cell-mediated immunity is the major factor in controlling the infection and in limiting viraemia.

Epidemiology

The prevalence of antibody positivity varies in different communities and is particularly related to socioeconomic status, the highest levels occurring in the lowest socioeconomic groups. In the United Kingdom approximately 50% of adults have antibody (which indicates latent infection). Infection is common during the first five years of life and about one half of the total number of infections occur in children. There is then little increase in antibody prevalence until late teenage when the infection rate increases again; this is probably due mainly to sexual transmission of the virus. The prevalence of antibody in populations of promiscuous individuals approaches 100%.

Diseases caused by CMV

CMV is a major cause of congenital abnormality. This important effect of the virus is described in Chapter 15.

In children and adults with normal immunity CMV is rarely a problem and, indeed, most primary infections are totally asymptomatic and recurrences are inapparent. The primary infection occasionally causes a mononucleosis-like illness in young adults and this should be suspected in cases in which heterophil antibodies are absent (i.e. the Paul–Bunnell test is negative). As with EBV-associated mononucleosis the febrile period is often accompanied by a low grade hepatitis. A similar mononucleosis-like syndrome may occur after transfusion with fresh blood and this has been particularly common after open-heart surgery. This condition, the post-perfusion syndrome, presents with fever and lymphadenopathy 30–40 days after transfusion and is associated with cytomegaloviraemia and seroconversion to the virus.

Disseminated infection in the immunocompromised may lead to widespread disease which may be fatal. The likelihood of this developing and the prospects for overcoming the infection depend to a large extent on the degree and reversibility of the immunocompromise. Thus the patient with the acquired immune deficiency syndrome (AIDS) who has very poor cellular immune mechanisms is much more vulnerable than the less compromised renal transplant recipient in whom the immunosuppressive therapy can be reduced to

allow him to overcome the infection. CMV pneumonitis with increasing hypoxia can be rapidly progressive in these patients and this complication is a major cause of death after bone marrow transplantation. In AIDS a destructive retinitis caused by replication of the virus in the retina may lead to blindness and other manifestations such as colitis and encephalopathy are occasionally seen.

Laboratory diagnosis

Human CMV is highly species specific and it has not been shown to infect another animal host. This has caused problems in producing specific animal antisera but the advent of monoclonal antibodies has allowed the introduction of immunofluorescence as a rapid diagnostic test which can be applied directly to clinical material or to infected cell cultures. Virus can be isolated in human embryonic fibroblasts and it produces a focal CPE which, depending on the virus titre in the inoculum, usually takes 1–3 weeks to appear. The virus does not grow in epithelioid cells *in vitro*; this is curious as epithelial cells are often infected *in vivo*. Histology often provides a good basis for diagnosing CMV infection and immunofluorescence and/or culture can be used for confirmation. In neonates and immunocompromised patients who have disseminated CMV the virus can be readily detected in, and cultured from, many sites including throat swabs, urine, blood, semen and tissues such as liver and kidney. The virus is sometimes reactivated from its latent state and asymptomatic infection can be detected in samples of saliva, urine, semen and, during pregnancy, on the cervix. Serological tests (complement fixation, neutralizing and immunofluorescent antibody tests) are useful in diagnosing clinically apparent or asymptomatic infections and tests for virus specific IgM are important in demonstrating recent and continuing infection.

Prevention and treatment

An important aspect in the prevention of CMV related diseases is donor screening. Antibody testing of blood donors allows the compilation of a CMV-negative donor panel and this blood should be used preferentially in neonates and in those undergoing bone marrow transplantation. Other aspects of prevention and treatment of CMV are still at the investigational stages. A prototype subunit vaccine has shown some apparent effect in lessening the disease in infected renal transplant patients but it did not prevent their infection. CMV specific immunoglobulin has been given prophylactically to the immunocompromised and therapeutically in disseminated infection with encouraging results. The effects of antiviral compounds in CMV pneumonitis in bone marrow transplant recipients have been disappointing until recently. Of two compounds currently on trial, foscarnet and gancyclovir (DHPG), the latter is showing considerable promise in the treatment of pneumonitis in renal transplant recipients and in the control of CMV retinitis in AIDS patients.

Epstein–Barr virus (EBV)

EBV was was first isolated in 1964 from tissue obtained from cases of African Burkitt's lymphoma. The peculiar geographical distribution of this tumour prompted the search for a viral aetiology. Following identification of the virus as a member of the Herpetiviridae it soon became clear that, in addition to its firm association with Burkitt's lymphoma, the virus was prevalent in all communities. Seroepidemiological studies established the causative role of EBV in Paul–Bunnell positive infectious mononucleosis. Although EBV is morphologically similar to the other herpesviruses it is unique in the fact that it can only be cultured in B lymphocytes or in lymphoblastoid lines of B cell origin. These cells are grown in suspension culture and the virus is not normally cytopathic. B cells from individuals who have never been infected with EBV cannot be grown in continuous culture. Infection with the virus effectively immortalizes (transforms) them and they will then grow as continuous cells. Most of the viral DNA in transformed B cells remains in circular, non-integrated, form as an episome. Virus or antigen production is detected by immunofluorescence.

Immunology

The acute phase of the illness is characterized by a relative or absolute neutropenia and increase in circulating mononuclear cells. These atypical mononuclear cells are, in fact T lymphocytes undergoing transformation to lymphoblasts in response to EBV replication in B lymphocytes. Demonstration of these atypical lymphocytes, which normally account for more than 20% of the total leucocyte count, is in itself a reasonable basis for the diagnosis of EBV infection. The presence of EBV replication within the immune system leads to transient polyclonal B cell activation and this probably accounts for the heterophil antibody reaction (Paul–Bunnell test—see below) and the occasional anamnestic response to some other antigens.

Epidemiology

Following recovery from infectious mononucleosis the virus is excreted intermittently in the oropharynx for 12–18 months. This probably represents the major source of infection for others and transmission is thought to occur mainly by kissing. As would be anticipated, therefore, teenagers are particularly likely to acquire the infection. Antibody prevalence in the population depends on socioeconomic status; in most western communities 60–70% of young adults are latently infected.

EBV related diseases

The important association between EBV and Burkitt's lymphoma is discussed in Chapter 19. Asymptomatic infections are common, particularly in children, and infectious mononucleosis (glandular fever) is normally benign and uncomplicated. The incubation period is probably between 14 and 28 days. The main clinical features are fever, lymphadenopathy (particularly in the cervical region), pharyngitis (which may have an associated exudate similar to that caused by streptococci), fatigue and malaise. These symptoms and signs vary in their duration from days to several weeks. On rare occasions the patient may proceed to a debilitating post-viral syndrome which may last for months. Liver function tests are abnormal at the acute stage although jaundice is rare; this often becomes evident in reduced tolerance to alcohol. On occasions ampicillin is given in error to individuals at the acute stage of the illness, usually because the pharyngeal exudate has been mistaken for a streptococcal sore throat. This is very likely to induce a prompt drug reaction with a widespread rash. This hypersensitivity to ampicillin is only transient; it probably results from viral impairment of lymphocyte function and penicillins are not contraindicated after recovery. The main complication of infectious mononucleosis is splenic rupture; the spleen becomes enlarged during the acute stage and may be damaged by over-vigorous abdominal examination. For this reason, the temptation to allow large groups of medical students to palpate the patient's abdomen should be resisted. Encephalitis, which may involve the brain stem, thrombocytopenia and haemolytic anaemia are rare complications.

Laboratory diagnosis

The most convenient and commonly used diagnostic test for EBV infection is the heterophil antibody test or Paul–Bunnell. This is also available as a screening test (Monospot). The heterophil antibody produced at the acute stage of EBV infection is an agglutinin for sheep erythrocytes. In the Paul–Bunnell test, the patient's serum is first adsorbed with guinea pig kidney homogenate to remove cross-reacting antibodies that may be present in other conditions such as serum sickness. The specificity of the heterophil antibody is confirmed by the fact that it can be removed by adsorption with bovine erythrocytes. The heterophil antibody titre is the highest dilution of serum to agglutinate the erythrocytes. Immunofluorescence, using EBV-infected lymphoblastoid cells, can be used to detect specific antibodies to viral antigens. Antibodies to the viral capsid antigen (VCA) rise early in the disease and persist for life. Detection of IgM antibody to VCA can be used to diagnose a recent or continuing infection. Antibodies to the nuclear antigen (EBNA) rise later in the disease (about one month after onset) and persist at a low level for life. Children under the age of six years do not normally produce heterophil antibodies and detection of viral specific antibodies is the most important approach to diagnosis. Virus isolation is not normally required in routine diagnosis but, if necessary, it is best achieved by immunofluorescence on inoculated cord blood lymphocytes.

Prevention and treatment

No vaccine or immunoglobulin is available for prophylaxis. Although the virus coded DNA polymerase of EBV is sensitive to acyclovir (presumably after phosphorylation by host cell enzymes), and this drug reduces the number of antigen bearing cells in infected cultures, acyclovir is not normally required in the management of an infected patient.

Further reading

Epstein M. A. and Achong B. G. (1979) *The Epstein-Barr virus*. Springer-Verlag, Berlin.

Ho M. (1982) *Cytomegalovirus: Biology and Infection*. Plenum Press, New York.

Nahmias A. J., Dowdle W. R. and Schinazi R. F. (1981) *The Human Herpesviruses*. Elsevier, New York.

Chapter 11
Enteroviruses

Enteroviruses are small (20–30 nm) RNA viruses which form a major subgroup of the picornavirus family. They are distinguished from rhinoviruses by their resistance to acid and their optimal growth temperature (37°C). As the name indicates they readily infect, and are shed from, the intestinal tract. The main classes of enteroviruses are listed in Table 11.1. They cause a wide spectrum of diseases including paralysis, mild meningitis, pyrexia, exanthema, myositis, oral ulceration and widespread damage in the newborn. Many infections are, however, totally asymptomatic particularly in children.

Table 11.1 The main classes of enteroviruses.

Class	Number of serotypes
Poliovirus	3
Coxsackie virus	
Group A	23
Group B	6
Echovirus	31
Enterovirus	Types 68–72

Poliomyelitis

Poliomyelitis is an acute infectious disease caused by poliovirus types 1–3 which are antigenically distinct. In its most severe form it affects the central nervous system and may cause flaccid paralysis by destruction of motor neurons (anterior horn cells) in the spinal cord and/or brain stem. Most infections in children are asymptomatic (*c.* 90%) and the majority of clinical attacks produce only a minor febrile illness. In adults, the risk of paralysis is greater.

Pathogenesis

The mouth is the portal of entry, as with all enteroviruses, and primary multiplication occurs in the oropharynx or intestinal wall. Virus becomes detectable in the throat and faeces before the onset of illness and continues to be excreted, despite the development of high antibody levels, for several weeks. Viraemia is present in asymptomatic individuals, and those with disease, before the onset of antibody production. It is this viraemic phase which may lead to invasion of the meninges, spinal cord or brain stem. Although the virus may be widely disseminated in the central nervous system, replication in anterior horn cells may be lytic and lead to destruction of these important components of the motor pathway. This may lead to localized or extensive loss of function and flaccid paralysis of the muscle groups concerned. Loss of balance between antagonistic muscle groups leads to spasm of the unaffected muscles and this may result in contractures which may cause further handicap.

Neuronal damage is likely to be enhanced or triggered iatrogenically by intervention during the incubation period or prodromal illness. Tonsillectomy at this time predisposes to respiratory failure due to invasion of motor neurons in the medulla oblongata and cervical spinal cord and gluteal injections, particularly with alum based preparations, increase the risk of leg paralysis. When poliomyelitis was epidemic in the United Kingdom inappropriate injection of penicillin at the stage of the minor illness, in the mistaken belief that this was caused by streptococcal infection, resulted in cases of permanent paralysis. These procedures may enhance the entry of virus into peripheral nerves and thus facilitate access to the spinal cord and brain. The invasion of anterior horn cells is accompanied by focal and perivascular infiltrations of lymphocytes with some accompanying polymorphonuclear neutrophils (PMNs) and plasma cells. The associated inflammatory response may enhance the functional loss at the acute stage and some improvement may be observed as this subsides.

Immunology

Immunity is permanent to the serotype causing the infection and there may be some heterotypic resistance to the other types. Neutralizing antibody develops early in the disease process, often before the onset of symptoms, and nervous system effects may ensue despite the presence of high levels of antibody. This indicates that the invasion occurs at the early viraemic stage prior to antibody production.

Epidemiology

Poliomyelitis has a worldwide distribution although the successful immunization campaigns maintained in developed countries have largely eliminated the disease. Humans are the only known natural reservoir of infection. As with other enteroviruses, infection is common throughout the year in the tropics and during summer and autumn in temperate climates. Transmission is favoured by poor hygiene and sanitation. Faecal contamination of water supplies and food, possibly enhanced by vectors, e.g. house-flies, leads to widespread epidemics in developing countries. The viruses can survive for prolonged periods in sewage and even in chlorinated water if sufficient organic debris is present.

Clinical effects

The incubation period is usually 7–14 days but a range of 3–35 days has been recorded. Abortive poliomyelitis is the commonest clinical manifestation and the patient suffers only the minor illness. The symptoms are influenza-like in nature and fever, malaise, drowsiness, headache, nausea, vomiting, constipation and sore throat may all be featured. The patient recovers within a few days and the diagnosis can only be made by laboratory investigations. The minor illness may be accompanied by aseptic meningitis and in common with other types of enteroviral meningitis this is usually benign and resolves in 2–10 days without sequelae. The major illness follows on from the minor illness often with two or three symptom-free days intervening. It may also arise *de novo*, without the preceding minor illness. The appearance of asymmetrical paralysis is often accompanied by signs of meningeal irritation. Flaccid paralysis and loss of muscle tone often accompanied by painful spasm of uninvolved muscles, but with no obvious sensory loss, are characteristically found on examination. Respiratory embarrassment may indicate the involvement of the medulla oblongata and the motor neurons supplying the phrenic nerves. Paralysis develops over several days and then, as described earlier, some recovery may be gained. Effects persisting for more than six months are permanent.

Laboratory diagnosis

The cerebrospinal fluid usually shows the changes which are typical of viral meningitis. The cell count is raised (10–200/μl); early in the disease these are mainly PMNs but a lymphocytic picture soon predominates. The protein content is raised (40–50 mg/dl) and the glucose is normal. Virus may be cultured in primary or continuous cells derived from humans or monkeys and the rapidly destructive cytopathic effect can be specifically identified by neutralization with type-specific antisera. Throat swabs (or washings) and rectal swabs or faeces are the main sources of material. Virus is not usually recovered from the CSF, in contrast to infections with coxsackie and echoviruses. Histological examination of the spinal cord of fatal cases will reveal the destruction and inflammatory process in regions of the affected motor neurons and, if death has occurred at the acute stage, it may be possible to isolate virus from those sites.

Neutralization tests, in which acute and convalescent serum samples are mixed with known concentrations of laboratory strains of polioviruses and then adsorbed to permissive monolayers, are the most useful system for confirming recent infection (see Table 6.1). This technique can also be used to assess the level of protective immunity in individuals prior to active immunization.

Prevention of infection

Live attenuated and inactivated vaccines, containing respectively the three serotypes of the virus and their antigens, are in routine use.

The formaldehyde-inactivated vaccine (Salk) is given subcutaneously and the primary course consists of four doses (three doses 4–8 weeks apart and the fourth 6–12 months later). This produces protective immunity in >95% of recipients but booster doses are necessary periodically throughout life and every 2–3 years in those at high risk. This inactivated vaccine stimulates IgG antibody production and therefore protects the nervous system but the absence of local immunity in the intestine means that wild virus is able to implant and replicate. Thus the individual concerned is protected against the major illness but may act as an infectious source for others.

Live vaccine (Sabin) contains carefully controlled levels of attenuated virus types 1–3 grown in human diploid cell culture. Addition of magnesium chloride results in stabilization so that it can be kept at 4°C for one year or one month at ambient temperatures. An important advantage of this type of vaccine is the route of administration. It is given orally and this leads to the production of secretory IgA in the gut in addition to circulating IgM and IgG. This renders the intestines resistant to reinfection. The establishment of active replication of the vaccine strains in the intestines has advantages and disadvantages. The viruses appear in the faeces in infectious form and may thus be transmitted to others. While this may result in a conveyance of immunity to susceptible contacts it may also cause an occasional case of paralytic poliomyelitis. The reason for this is that passage of the viruses in the human may cause the vaccine strains to revert to a virulent form (particularly types 2 and 3). Fortunately this type of disease is very rare but it is important to ensure that parents have been immunized before initiating a course of oral vaccine in their children. Live vaccine protects >95% of recipients and, although replication of the three types is likely to yield lasting immunity, the presence of other viruses in the intestine may prevent establishment of infection by interference. For this reason it is important to administer the vaccine on more than one occasion and it is normally included with the triple vaccination programme in the first year of life.

In keeping with the general policy regarding live vaccines, oral polio vaccine must not be given to those with immunocompromise. Deficiency in humoral antibody production is particularly likely to lead to paralysis from dissemination of the vaccine to the central nervous system. The inactivated vaccine should be used in these individuals. Although oral vaccine is not contraindicated for pregnant women who are at serious risk of acquiring poliomyelitis it is sensible in others to delay immunization until the end of the pregnancy or offer inactivated vaccine.

Coxsackievirus infections

Coxsackieviruses are divided into subgroups A (23 serotypes) and B (6 serotypes) mainly on the basis of their growth pattern in suckling mice (see below).

Epidemiology

The viruses are ubiquitous and have similar characteristics to polioviruses in that they are prevalent throughout the year in the tropics and are most prevalent in the summer and autumn in temperate countries. Isolation of many different types is possible from sewage and transmission is faecal–oral. Once introduced into a household the viruses are likely to infect the family members although not all develop symptoms.

Pathogenesis

As with polioviruses, the mouth is the portal of entry of the viruses. They are present in the throat early in the course of infection and are usually excreted in faeces for several weeks after recovery. Viraemia has been detected at an early stage and this results in dissemination of the virus to distant sites in the body and accounts for the varied syndromes associated with coxsackievirus infection.

Clinical effects

The incubation period varies between two and nine days and this may be followed by one of several different disease manifestations.

Herpangina

This is an acute pharyngitis, caused by several serotypes of coxsackie A viruses, which is characterized by the formation of discrete vesicles, surrounded by a halo of inflammation, on the fauces, palate, uvula, tonsils and back of the tongue. It is associated with fever and occasionally anorexia, vomiting and abdominal pain. The illness is self-limiting after a few days.

Hand, foot and mouth disease

This is another vesicular manifestation of coxsackie A viruses (mainly A16) in which there are vesicles in the mouth and, classically, similar vesicles on the hands and feet. The skin vesicles are round, white and opaque and associated with a surrounding area of acute inflammation. Unlike herpesvirus vesicles, they heal without rupture and crusting. Atypical presentations are common and vesicles can often be found on other parts of the body. If the infection occurs in babies large florid lesions may be present in the nappy area. Systemic upset is usually mild or absent and the disease resolves after a few days.

Bornholm disease

Bornholm disease (epidemic myalgia, epidemic pleurodynia) is caused by group B coxsackieviruses. The patient usually presents with localized, acute pain in the chest or abdomen and the severity may be such that a diagnosis of pleurisy or acute abdomen may result. Fever is usually present and there is often preceding malaise, headache and anorexia. The pain is intensified by movement and resolves naturally within a few days.

Myocarditis

The tropism of group B coxsackieviruses for muscle tissue occasionally extends to cardiac muscle. This may result in arrhythmias and cardiac failure. The disease is usually self-limiting provided the patient survives the acute stage but there is some evidence that it may occasionally proceed to chronic cardiomyopathy and relapses are not uncommon.

Aseptic meningitis

As described above for poliovirus infection, aseptic meningitis is normally benign and uncomplicated. Collectively, the enteroviruses account for the majority of cases of aseptic meningitis and a significant number of these are due to coxsackieviruses of both subgroups. Fever, malaise, headache, nausea and abdominal pain in varying combinations are followed within 1–2 days by neck and/or back stiffness often with vomiting. There may also be some associated mild muscle weakness. The cerebrospinal fluid abnormalities are similar to those of poliomyelitis.

Neonatal disease

Infection with coxsackie B viruses may be acquired by babies during the birth process if the viruses are present in the mother's faeces. Viraemia occasionally results particularly if the baby is born prematurely. Myocarditis, encephalitis and hepatitis due to extensive replication of the virus may be preceded by lethargy, feeding difficulty, diarrhoea and vomiting. The myocarditis may lead to cardiac failure and respiratory distress and the disease may be rapidly fatal.

Febrile illnesses and head colds

Coxsackieviruses are often isolated from people with minor febrile illnesses occurring during the summer and autumn and it is not uncommon for family members of a case of herpangina or hand, foot and mouth disease to suffer this type of nondescript illness. Some of the enteroviruses, including coxsackieviruses A10, A21 and A24 and B3, have been associated with common colds.

Diabetes mellitus

There is a significant association between the presence of antibody to coxsackievirus B4 and the development of acute onset diabetes mellitus. In mice, another Picornavirus (encephalomyocarditis virus) induces acute diabetes by destruction of the islets of Langerhans. The causal role for coxsackie in human diabetes awaits further evaluation.

Laboratory diagnosis

Coxsackieviruses are highly infective for newborn mice. Certain strains (B1–6, A7, 9, 16 and 24) also grow in monkey kidney cells. Viruses from the two groups can be distinguished by the pattern of disease produced in the mice. Group A induce a widespread myositis in the skeletal muscles which results in flaccid paralysis. Characteristically, the mice are seen to pull themselves along by their front limbs and to drag their flaccid hind limbs. If they are placed on their backs they are often unable to return to the normal position. Group B viruses produce an encephalitis which may cause spastic paralysis with increased muscle tone. In addition there is visible necrosis of fat deposits and histological evidence of widespread viraemia with pancreatitis, hepatitis and myocarditis.

The viruses may be isolated from the throat of patients in the first few days of the illness and from the faeces for several weeks after. Cerebrospinal fluid often yields virus at the acute stage. Specimens are inoculated intracerebrally or intraperitoneally in suckling mice (<24 hours old) and also into monkey kidney cell cultures. Effects in the mice are normally seen within 3–8 days with group A viruses and 5–14 days with group B. Cytopathic effects in cell culture appear in 5–14 days. Viruses are identified by neutralization tests.

Antibodies to the viruses appear early in the course of the illness and demonstration of seroconversion or a rise in neutralizing antibody can provide a retrospective diagnosis. In view of the large numbers of serotypes involved this is likely to be a tedious task and serological diagnosis is not routinely available for these viruses. The advent of hybridization probes should greatly assist in evaluating the role of coxsackieviruses in chronic diseases including cardiomyopathy and diabetes mellitus.

Echovirus infections

Echovirus is an acronym for enteric cytopathogenic human orphan virus. This name was applied after the discovery of viruses in the human gut which were cytopathic in certain cell cultures and yet were unassociated with any particular disease. There are now over 35 known serotypes although not all cause human illness and, similar to coxsackieviruses, they are responsible for attacks of aseptic meningitis, febrile illnesses with and without exanthema and common colds. They parallel coxsackieviruses in their epidemiological pattern and pathogenesis of infection.

Clinical effects

The frequency of isolating these viruses from the faeces of normal individuals has caused considerable difficulty in assessing their possible role in diarrhoeal illness and minor febrile attacks. In outbreaks the higher rate of isolation from those affected compared to controls together with the development of neutralizing antibody to that particular virus has been used as the method of judging significance. Certain serotypes have been associated with outbreaks of aseptic meningitis and type 11 has caused severe meningitis in infants in neonatal intensive care units. The effects of echoviruses in premature neonates can be similar to those of coxsackie B viruses. The rashes occurring during the course of some infections do not normally have characteristic features and vary from a few papules on the trunk to scattered vesicles. Volunteer studies have shown that echovirus type 28 has the capacity to produce head colds.

Laboratory diagnosis

Echoviruses produce a marked cytopathic effect in monkey kidney cells and the viruses can be typed using specific antisera. As there are so many serotypes it is usually convenient to employ pools of antisera, each pool containing antibodies to several serotypes. When a pool has been shown to produce neutralization, the virus is then tested with each of the antisera used to compile the pool. Because of the large number of types, serological diagnosis is not normally attempted.

Other enteroviruses

Recently several new enteroviruses have been identified and these have been numbered sequentially (68–72). Enterovirus 68 has been isolated from the respiratory tracts of children with bronchiolitis and pneumonia. Enterovirus 70 is the main cause of acute haemorrhagic conjunctivitis (although coxsackieviruses and echoviruses occasionally produce this syndrome). This disease appeared as a new entity in Africa and Southeast Asia in 1969–71. Since then it has become endemic in a number of parts of the world. Its onset is heralded by sub-conjunctival haemorrhages and there may be associated epithelial keratitis and occasionally lumbar radiculomyelopathy. The incubation period is one day and the symptoms and signs last for 8–10 days and usually resolve without long term complications. It is highly infectious and the clinical effects are most evident in adults.

Enterovirus 71 has been characterized as a major cause of central nervous system disease and it has been isolated from cases of meningitis, encephalitis and paralysis. It has also been recorded as a cause of hand, foot and mouth disease in Sweden and Japan.

Prevention of infection with enteroviruses other than polio

There are no specific vaccines or antisera available for prevention of infection. In certain situations, particularly hospital outbreaks, it may be necessary to consider cohorting of patients and/or staff to try to reduce nosocomial transmission.

There is no specific antiviral therapy for any of the enteroviral infections.

Further reading

Melnick J. L. (1982) Enteroviruses. In: *Viral Infections of Humans. Epidemiology and Control*, Evans A.S. (Ed). Plenum Medical Book Company, New York.

Ray C. G. (1983) Coxsackievirus and echovirus infections. In: *Infectious Diseases*, 3rd edition. Hoeprich P.D. (Ed). Harper and Row, New York.

Chapter 12
Encephalitis

Encephalitis (inflammation of the brain) may result from infection with a number of different viruses. In the newborn, immaturity of immune responses renders the brain vulnerable to viraemias which are less likely to occur in the older host. In older children and adults, fusion of the bones of the skull encloses the brain in a rigid container. While providing protection for the brain this allows very little capacity for expansion if the brain should become inflamed with consequent oedema. A rise in intracranial pressure from encephalitis leads to expansion of the brain in the only direction possible, through the foramen magnum. This may produce pressure of the medulla oblongata against the foramen and thus inhibit the function of the vital centres (respiratory and vasomotor) in the reticular formation of the brain stem. This phenomenon (coning), if allowed to progress without surgical or chemotherapeutic measures to decompress the brain, is likely to lead to sudden death. In addition to the inflammatory effects of encephalitis, there is no regeneration of neurons that have been destroyed by the infection. For these reasons, therefore, encephalitis is potentially the most serious complication of all virus infections.

Viral encephalitis may result from two main pathogenetic mechanisms. Viral invasion of the brain with a cytocidal virus may result in destruction of brain substance due to local or generalized growth of the virus. This invasive (polioclastic) type of infection is caused by arthropod-borne viruses (arboviruses), rabies and as a rare complication of herpes simplex virus infections. The second major type, (post-infectious encephalomyelitis) develops during the convalescent stages of a number of common viral diseases (e.g. measles, rubella, mumps, varicella) and after certain immunizations (e.g. vaccinia, brain-based rabies vaccine). The pathogenesis differs from the invasive type of encephalitis in the important fact that brain damage is not the direct result of viral replication. The disease is caused by demyelination and associated inflammation which resembles an auto-allergic reaction to brain antigens. This process, which commences several days after the acute stage of the illness is thought to be triggered by some degree of replication of the virus in the brain during the height of the illness.

The situation with brain-based rabies vaccines is more easily understood as these older forms of vaccine incorporated large amounts of brain antigens and, in view of the large number of repeated doses required, would have been particularly likely to sensitize the individual to neuronal tissue.

In addition to the two main types of acute encephalitis there is a collection of conditions known as slow virus diseases. These are subacute degenerations of the brain which are progressive and fatal following a prolonged incubation period of years rather than months. They include the retrovirus infection of sheep (visna), the spongiform encephalopathies (scrapie, kuru and Creutzfeldt–Jakob syndrome), subacute sclerosing panencephalitis (SSPE) and progressive multifocal leucoencephalopathy (PML).

Invasive encephalitides

Arboviral infections

More than 350 viruses from several different families are transmitted, by blood-sucking arthropods, from one vertebrate host to another. Many of these zoonotic viruses can infect humans in addition to domestic and wild animals and many can replicate in the tissues of their arthropod vectors without evidence of disease or damage. All have an RNA genome and most have a surrounding lipid-containing membrane. Individual viruses are named after the disease (e.g. dengue, yellow fever) or after the area where the virus was first characterized (e.g. St Louis encephalitis, West Nile fever). The main groups of arboviruses are shown in Table 12.1.

Three main types of disease are produced by arboviruses:

1 Fever of an undifferentiated type sometimes with a maculopapular rash and usually benign.

2 Haemorrhagic fevers often severe and frequently fatal.

3 Encephalitis.

The haemorrhagic fever viruses are described in Chapter 17. Two families of arboviruses are associated with encephalitis.

Togaviruses. These are spherical particles containing a single-stranded RNA genome and are surrounded by a lipid-containing membrane. Group A (alphaviruses) are 40–80 nm diameter, are inactivated by proteases, and all multiply in arthropods. Group B (flaviviruses) are smaller (30–50 nm), are not inactivated by proteases and do not all

Table 12.1 Arboviruses

Family	Genus	Viruses
Togaviridae	Alphavirus	Group A: Chikungunya, eastern equine encephalitis, Mayaro, O'Nyong-Nyong, Ross River, Semliki Forest, Sindbis, western equine and Venezuelan equine encephalitis viruses
	Flavivirus	Group B: Brazilian encephalitis, dengue, Japanese B encephalitis, Ilheus, Kyasanur Forest disease, louping ill, Murray Valley encephalitis, Omsk haemorrhagic fever, Powassan, St. Louis encephalitis, tick-borne encephalitis, US bat salivary gland, West Nile fever, yellow fever, and Zika viruses
Bunyaviridae	Bunyavirus	Anopheles A and B, California, Guama, Simbu (oropouche) and Turlock viruses
	Phlebovirus	Sandfly (phlebotomus) fever viruses
	Nairovirus	Crimean-Congo haemorrhagic fever, Nairobi sheep disease and Sakhalin viruses
	Uukuvirus	Uukuniemi and Hantaan viruses
Reoviridae	Orbivirus	African horse sickness, blue tongue and Colorado tick fever viruses
Rhabdoviridae	Vesiculovirus	Hart Park, Kern Canyon and vesicular stomatitis viruses
Arenoviridae	Arenovirus	Junin, Lassa, Machupo and Pichinde viruses
Nodaviridae		Nodamura virus (an insect pathogen that can infect mammals)

replicate in the vector. Members of each group are antigenically related.

Bunyaviruses. A single negative-stranded, segmented RNA genome is enclosed in spherical particles that are surrounded by a lipid-containing envelope (90–100 nm diameter). The envelope has surface projections (10 nm) composed of glycoprotein in the form of hollow cylinders. All replicate in arthropods.

Pathogenesis and clinical presentations

The arthropod vector deposits virus directly into a capillary in the course of obtaining a blood meal. This results in viraemia which produces widespread infection in the reticuloendothelial system and vascular endothelium. Following an incubation period of 3–21 days there is a major viraemia which often produces an acute onset of illness with malaise, headache, nausea, vomiting, myalgia and fever. If the virus enters the central nervous system at this stage, the symptoms and signs of encephalitis may develop within 24–48 hours. Mental function is impaired, with dysarthria and memory loss, and the patient becomes drowsy and may become progressively more deeply comatose. Convulsions are common and neck stiffness may be present. The encephalitic manifestations may present without the preceding prodromal febrile illness. Many individuals have asymptomatic or mild infections but the viraemia, present for several days, provides a source of infection which may be transmitted to others by biting arthropods. The severity of the disease depends on the virus concerned, on the host response and the degree of involvement of the brain. Some viruses, e.g. California virus, rarely cause death while others, e.g. Japanese B encephalitis, may produce 80% mortality in the older age groups. Sequelae of infection may include mental deterioration, personality changes, paralysis, aphasia and cerebellar signs.

Pathological changes consist of degeneration of neurons with neuronophagia and occasionally destruction of surrounding glial tissue. There is perivascular and meningeal infiltration of mononuclear cells.

Immune response

Humoral antibodies develop within 1–2 weeks of the onset of illness and may be detected by haemagglutination inhibition, complement fixation, neutralization and precipitation tests. Neutralizing antibodies are the most serotype specific, generally persist for many years and confer long term protection to that particular virus. Haemagglutination inhibiting and complement fixing antibodies are group specific and do not always clearly distinguish between infections by different members of a specific genus.

Epidemiology and specific infections

In severe epidemics of arboviral encephalitis the proportion of clinically apparent cases to asymptomatic infections is approximately 1:1000. Most infections occur in mammals or birds and humans are infected as accidental hosts. Mosquitoes and ticks serve as reservoirs of infection and provide the means of dissemination. As the viruses can usually replicate in these vectors this serves to amplify the infectious dose of virus to be transmitted to the next vertebrate. Arbovirus infections are more prevalent in areas with a high density of mosquitoes and ticks and their incidence shows considerable geographic variation. In tropical countries, where the vectors are present throughout the year, arboviruses cycle continuously between the arthropods and animal reservoirs. In temperate climates the mechanism for overwintering of the viruses is not fully understood. Three possibilities exist to explain this:

1 The viruses may survive in hibernating arthropods.
2 Persistent viraemia may occur in small mammals, birds and snakes.
3 Transovarial transmission may be an important route of infection from parents of offspring in vectors (this is known to occur in ticks). In addition to these mechanisms, migrating birds may reintroduce viruses from tropical areas. The seasonal variations in the appearance of the arthropod vectors means that arboviral infections are seen during the summer and autumn in temperate countries. Epidemics are particularly likely when climatic conditions and ecologic circumstances (e.g. flooding) are optimal for arthropod breeding and hatching.

Equine encephalitides

The equine encephalitides eastern equine encephalitis (EEE), western equine encephalitis (WEE) and Venezuelan equine encephalitis (VEE) are transmitted to horses or humans by culicine mosquitoes from a mosquito–bird–mosquito cycle. An epizootic in horses often alerts physicians to an impending outbreak in humans; EEE and WEE are severe and often fatal in the horse while VEE usually produces less serious disease. St Louis encephalitis (SLE) and Japanese B encephalitis (JBE) have similar mosquito–bird–mosquito cycles. SLE infects horses asymptomatically while the major vertebrate host for JBE, other than man, is the pig. California virus encephalitis, although first described in that state, is most prevalent in the Mid-west states. It is transmitted by Aedes mosquitoes and most illness is seen in children and teenagers. Convulsions are common but the mortality rate is very low. Following ingestion of infected blood the mosquito acquires an infection in the cells of the mid gut. After replication in this site, viraemia results in transfer of the virus to distant organs, mainly the salivary glands and the nervous system. The infection persists, without disease, for the life of the mosquito (several weeks). Only the female mosquitoes feed on blood and the persistent infection in the salivary glands means that one female can infect many vertebrate hosts.

Tick-borne encephalitis complex

Russian spring-summer encephalitis. This disease occurs mainly in early summer in those exposed, in uncleared forest, to ticks of the Ixodes genus. The virus can be transmitted transovarially in the ticks and can also persist through the winter in hibernating ticks or in bats and hedgehogs. Infected goats can excrete virus in the milk for long periods and humans can become infected from drinking unpasteurized milk. If encephalitis develops it can be severe, involving particularly the bulbar region and spinal cord, with the development of ascending paralysis or hemiplegia. The mortality in overt cases is approximately 30%.

Louping ill. This is a tick-borne infection (*Ixodes ricinus*) of Scottish sheep which occasionally results in human disease. The fatality rate is very low.

Tick-borne encephalitis (Central European encephalitis). This virus is antigenically related to Russian spring–summer encephalitis and louping ill virus. The illness is characteristically biphasic with an influenza-like prodrome leading after a short recovery period to meningoencephalitis, sometimes with paralysis.

Laboratory diagnosis

Virus occurs in the blood towards the end of the incubation period and for the first 1–2 days of illness. Isolation is normally attempted by intracerebral inoculation of newborn mice and identification of the virus involved can be ascertained by neutralization tests. Examination of acute and convalescent sera by HAI, CFT or neutralization tests may demonstrate a rising titre to a specific arbovirus. However, as indicated earlier, antigenic sharing may lead to confusion due to anamnestic responses to other arboviruses.

Prevention and treatment

There is no specific treatment for arboviral encephalitis. The major approach to prevention is to avoid contact with biting arthropods either by using insect repellents or mosquito nets. In some areas elimination of vectors by drainage and insecticides has been very successful. A vaccine against VEE prepared primarily for use in horses has been used with some success in humans.

Rabies

Rabies is an acute infection of the central nervous system which is almost invariably fatal. It is caused by a rhabdovirus which has morphological and biochemical similarities to vesicular stomatitis virus of cattle and to several animal, plant and insect viruses. The bullet-shaped capsid (180 × 70 nm) contains single-stranded RNA and is covered with a lipid-containing membrane from which protrude 10 nm spikes composed of glycoprotein. These surface glycoproteins stimulate the production of neutralizing and haemagglutination inhibiting antibody. The virus can be grown in cell culture and produces fulminating encephalitis when injected intracerebrally in laboratory rodents. Although it was originally thought to exist as a single serotype, different isolates vary in their virulence in animal hosts and monoclonal antibody reactions have revealed some minor antigenic variation.

Pathogenesis

Infection almost always results from an animal bite. The virus replicates in striated muscle or connective tissue at the site of inoculation and then enters the peripheral nervous system via the neuromuscular junctions. It then spreads to the central nervous system in the endoneurium of Schwann cells or associated tissue spaces. The incubation period may depend on the amount of inoculum, extent of tissue damage and distance of the bite from the brain. Incubation periods are shortest for those bitten on the face and neck. Infection can also result from inhalation of heavily contaminated material such as the air in bat-infested caves.

In the brain the virus produces neuronal destruction and hyperaemia in the cortex, basal ganglia, midbrain, pons and medulla oblongata. Rapid demyelination leads to degeneration of axons and myelin sheaths. In the spinal cord, neuronophagia and mononuclear cell infiltration involves particularly the posterior horns. Infected neurons characteristically contain eosinophilic, cytoplasmic inclusions (2–10 μm) known as Negri bodies; these are usually concentrated in Ammon's horn in the hippocampus although they are not always present. Following replication of the virus in the brain it enters the autonomic nervous system and is disseminated centrifugally to other organs including the salivary glands, adrenal medulla, lungs, heart and kidneys.

Epidemiology

The host range of rabies virus is very wide and, within endemic areas, many species of mammals may be infected. There is normally, however, a major animal vector; in Western Europe, the fox; in India, stray dogs and jackals; and in Latin America bats are the main hosts. A number of countries are rabies free as a result of tight import controls on animals. Maintenance of this situation is most easily achieved in islands as the only risk of introduction of the virus is through importation of animals from infected areas and this danger can be averted by strict customs controls. The United Kingdom and Ireland, Iceland, Japan and Australia are examples of rabies-free countries.

There are an estimated 15 000 cases of human rabies each year in the world and the majority of these occur in the Indian subcontinent and other parts of Southeast Asia. Human infection is incidental and does not contribute to the maintenance or transmission of the virus. Rabies exists in two epizootic forms: sylvatic, occurring in wild animals and urban involving unimmunized dogs and cats. Man is usually infected as a result of exposure to urban rabies and the risk is increased if the reservoir of stray dogs and cats is large. Mixing of urban strays with rural species provides the bridge between sylvatic and urban rabies. Most species infected with the virus develop clinical encephalitis and this often results in aggressive behaviour with an increased tendency to attack and bite. This phenomenon is vividly recorded in 'An elegy on the death of a mad dog' in Oliver Goldsmith's book *The Vicar of Wakefield*. This work dates from 1766 when rabies was endemic in England. The alteration of brain function may have other effects and a normally shy animal may become exceptionally friendly and approachable. This may be as dangerous as aggression in exposing humans to sylvatic rabies. Bats present a special problem because they may remain healthy carriers of the virus. They continue to excrete it in their saliva and may, therefore, disseminate infection for long periods. There is no evidence of human to human transmission via natural routes although transfer of the virus during corneal grafting has been recorded.

Clinical effects

The incubation period varies from 2–16 weeks although it may be occasionally as long as a year. Illness is heralded by the onset of a prodromal illness (2–10 days) consisting of malaise, anorexia, fatigue, headache and fever. A frequent and significant experience at this stage is the development of pain or paraesthesiae at the site of the bite and the patient may show increasing anxiety and apprehension. The prodrome is followed by the onset of neurologic effects which include hyperactivity, disorientation, seizures, hallucinations, bizarre behaviour and neck stiffness or paralysis. The hyperactivity is usually intermittent and may be precipitated by tactile, auditory, visual or other stimuli. Hydrophobia (fear of water) is characterized by severe painful spasms of the pharynx and larynx and is triggered by attempts to drink or eat or even the sight of water or food. These phases of hyperactivity of the nervous system are interspersed with quiet periods when the patient is usually co-operative and able to communicate. Muscle fasciculation may be observed in the region of the bite and hyperventilation is common. Increased salivation indicating autonomic nervous system dysfunction is usually present. Paralysis soon develops and this may be generalized or asymmetrical with maximal involvement in the bite area. In approximately 20% of cases the patient suffers predominantly from paralysis and the hyperactive phase is minimal or absent; this is known as dumb rabies. Death usually results from involvement of the vital centres in the brain stem which leads to cardiac or respiratory arrest. The median survival time after the onset of the nervous system effects is four days with a maximum of 20 days unless cardiorespiratory supportive measures are instituted. Most patients who have been kept alive in this way have suffered from further manifestations of the infection, e.g. myocarditis, pneumothorax and intravascular coagulation, but they have also been shown to develop specific antibody, at high titre, in the blood and CSF. The mortality in those who develop symptoms is virtually 100%. Recovery has been reported in two patients after prolonged periods in intensive care. Since these cases were described (in 1972) there have been no other successes recorded.

Laboratory diagnosis

Rapid and accurate diagnosis can be achieved by direct immunofluorescent staining of tissues using animal antisera. This technique is normally applied to corneal scrapes or skin biopsies in the human and to brain tissue from animals suspected of infection. Histological examination of brain material, particularly from Ammon's horn may reveal Negri bodies. Inoculation of tissue extracts or saliva, intracerebrally, in mice results in flaccid paralysis, encephalitis and death. The diagnosis can then be confirmed in the mice by demonstration of Negri bodies, immunofluorescence or by a neutralization test. Antibodies in the blood or CSF of animals or humans may be demonstrated by immunofluorescence, neutralization or complement fixation. Dogs and cats responsible for biting a human in an endemic area should, if possible, be observed for ten days to ensure that their health is maintained. If they develop signs suggestive of rabies they should be sacrificed and examined as described above. Wild animals are not normally observed in this way and the animal is killed and examined as soon as possible.

Prevention and treatment of infection

Active immunization against rabies dates from the late 19th century when Louis Pasteur, apparently successfully, applied post-exposure immunization to a boy, Joseph Meister, who had been severely bitten by a rabid animal. Pasteur used a crude vaccine made from the dried spinal cord of rabies-infected rabbits. This vaccine led to a range of different brain-based vaccines which were shown to be highly effective in pre- and post-exposure prophylaxis. Because of their nature, however, they all carried the burden of sensitization to nervous tissue antigens and the consequent risk of allergic encephalomyelitis (see below). A vaccine prepared in duck embryos reduced this risk but was found to be poorly immunogenic and also produced frequent local reactions. Recent development of a vaccine in human diploid cells has provided a potent and safe vaccine for immunization of those at risk of infection in addition to post-exposure protection of those bitten by rabid animals. This vaccine is prepared by growing attenuated virus in human fibroblasts and it is then concentrated, purified and inactivated with β-propiolactone. Pre-exposure prophylactic regimes depend on the level of possible exposure to the virus and the reader is referred to specialized vaccination schedules for details. Post-exposure prophylaxis is based on

1 Local wound debridement. The wound should not be sutured, but washing with soap and water should be followed by application of alcohol (40–70%) or an antiseptic, e.g. benzyl ammonium chloride.

2 Installation of human rabies immune globulin around the area of the wound; this should be supplemented with an intramuscular dose to confer short term (passive) protection.

3 Active immunization with rabies vaccine; this is administered intramuscularly (deltoid region) in five doses (days 0, 3, 7, 14 and 28).

None of the currently available antiviral drugs have had demonstrable benefit in rabies infection. As previously indicated, the only hope of treatment of established disease rests in prolonged intensive care.

Herpes simplex encephalitis

Involvement of the nervous system with herpes simplex viruses, though rare, accounts for most cases of sporadic encephalitis in the western world. Herpes simplex encephalitis (HSE) may be caused by either type 1 or type 2 and both produce similar effects of acute necrotization with associated inflammation and a consequent rise in intracranial pressure. In the neonate most cases result from type 2 infection acquired from the mother's genital tract while after the neonatal period, type 1 is the usual cause. Neonatal HSE is usually part of viraemic dissemination of the virus, cerebral involvement is widespread and the mortality is close to 100%. In older individuals the lesions are usually more localized but, if untreated, the mortality is approximately 70% and there is a high rate of neurological sequelae in the survivors.

Pathology and pathogenesis

Herpes simplex is highly destructive in the brain and areas of involvement show marked necrosis and associated softening and haemorrhage. In neonates this process is frequently widespread and may result in liquefaction of the brain. In children and adults the lesions are localized and asymmetric, the usual sites of involvement being the temporal lobes, the orbital portion of the frontal lobes and the limbic system. The cortex is infiltrated with lymphocytes, plasma cells and histiocytes with perivascular aggregates of these cells and there is usually lymphocytic infiltration of the meninges. The characteristic features of herpes simplex infection (intranuclear inclusions and margination of chromatin) are seen in infected neurons, astrocytes and oligodendrocytes and there is microglial proliferation. Herpes simplex antigens may be demonstrated by immunofluorescence and thin section electron microscopy reveals viral capsids.

There are a number of important unanswered questions concerning HSE. It is unknown why such a ubiquitous virus as herpes simplex type 1, on rare occasions, enters the brain to cause a destructive encephalitis. There is no evidence, from restriction endonuclease analysis of isolates from brain tissue, that the viruses involved are any different from the strains responsible for cold sores. There is also no evidence from studies on survivors of HSE that the disease has resulted from conditions of immunocompromise. Approximately 20–25% of patients who develop HSE due to the type 1 virus have a history of recurrent cold sores. While it is tempting to speculate that the temporal lobe invasion results from an ascending infection initiated in the trigeminal ganglion, autopsy studies have failed to confirm the path of infection from the appropriate ganglion to the cortical lesions and, in some cases, restriction endonuclease analysis of cortical isolates has shown them to be different viruses to those isolated from the lip. Another theory incriminates the olfactory nerves as the route of infection. Against this is the fact that the olfactory bulbs are frequently free from infection in patients who have died from HSE and it is rare to isolate the virus from the nasopharynx. In most cases of neonatal HSE the widespread cerebral involvement in association with viraemia and disease in other organs indicates that the virus has reached the brain and meninges through the vasculature. In some infants with encephalitis, however, there is no evidence of viraemic spread although almost all have herpes infection in the eye, mouth or skin. In these cases the encephalitis is often more focally distributed.

Epidemiology and immunology

HSE is one complication of herpes simplex virus infection. The epidemiology and immunology of these viruses is described in Chapter 9.

Clinical effects

HSE in the neonate is usually part of a generalized disease process. The initial signs usually appear within the first week although they may be present at birth or, rarely, appear as late as four weeks post partum. The early features are non-specific and include lethargy, fever or hypothermia, vomiting and poor feeding. Jaundice may be present as may purpura and respiratory effects, particularly apnoeic attacks, respiratory distress and cyanosis. Neurological effects include focal or generalized seizures, increased intracranial pressure with a bulging anterior fontanelle, opisthotonus, nerve palsies and flaccid or spastic paralysis. Progression to coma with decerebrate posturing and continuous seizures is usually rapidly followed by death.

In older children and adults the clinical picture is similar to that seen in other forms of encephalitis. The most common early manifestations are fever, headache and alterations in behaviour characterized by disorientation, confusion, memory-loss and reversion to childish behaviour. The early illness may be attributed to an influenza-like illness and the later effects may be confused with a psychiatric condition. It is most important that clinicians are aware of the clinical presentation of encephalitis, and its clear distinction from viral meningitis, so that specific therapy for HSE with acyclovir can be started as soon as possible. Progression of the illness is often dramatic with the appearance of delirium, hemiparesis and major seizures. Coma soon supervenes and death results from interruption of the function of the vital centres in the brain stem due to raised intracranial pressure. If the patient is deprived of specific therapy until consciousness is impaired or until localizing signs have developed, the likelihood of benefit from specific antiviral therapy is reduced and the risk of long term sequelae is increased.

Diagnosis

It is often impossible to obtain an early specific diagnosis of HSE. This condition is unique among the encephalitides in being potentially treatable provided specific therapy is started at an early stage. In the author's opinion, acyclovir therapy should be commenced when the suggestion of HSE is considered on clinical grounds and in many instances the diagnosis can be confirmed in retrospect by the development of changes in the temporal lobes viewed by computerized tomography scans and by serological changes to herpes simplex in the blood and CSF. Examination of the CSF often reveals a moderate increase in mononuclear cells but virus is rarely isolated and antibody levels are unhelpful at the acute stage. If craniotomy is performed as part of the investigation of a cerebral space-occupying lesion, brain biopsy material can be examined for herpes simplex by immunofluorescence, electron microscopy and virus culture.

Allergic (post-infectious) encephalitis

Experimental allergic encephalitis (EAE) can be induced in animals by mixing extracts of brain tissue with adjuvants and injecting it, intramuscularly, into other members of the same species. This produces a demyelinating encephalitis with widespread lesions in the brain and spinal cord associated with lymphocytic infiltration, perivascular cuffing of lymphocytes and oedema. EAE can be transferred passively to other animals by lymphoid cells, but not by serum, and probably represents a cell-mediated hypersensitivity to a nervous tissue antigen. As described earlier in this chapter, this type of encephalitic process was occasionally seen as a complication following the use of the older, brain-derived rabies vaccines in which brain antigens were known to be present. A similar disease is seen as a rare complication of some common infectious diseases and other vaccines, in particular vaccinia. Allergic encephalitis characteristically occurs several days after the acute phase of the initiating illness or vaccination and, unlike the invasive forms of encephalitis described previously, the disease is not associated with active replication of the virus in nervous tissue. As illustrated in the following examples, however, the immediate morbidity and mortality and the sequelae may be just as severe as those caused by the polioclastic encephalitides.

Post-vaccinial encephalitis

The realization that this rare, but significant, complication of smallpox vaccination was killing more people in the United Kingdom than were dying from imported smallpox led to the abandonment of routine vaccinations. The incidence varied in different countries but was usually in the region of three per million primary vaccinations. There were no discernible pre-disposing factors in those who suffered the complication. The onset was sudden and occurred about 12 days after vaccination with disorientation, confusion, seizures and progressive loss of consciousness leading to death in approximately 40% of patients. Many of the survivors were left with permanent nerve palsies and other sequelae.

Measles encephalitis

Although electroencephalographic (EEG) abnormalities are detectable in most patients with measles, the development of overt encephalitis occurs in approximately 0.1% of cases. The disease develops in the period 6–14 days after the onset of the rash and results in a mortality of 15% and residual morbidity in 25%. The evidence of EEG abnormality at the acute stage may provide the clue to the pathogenesis of measles encephalitis. If this indicates invasion of the brain, the transient presence of the virus may be sufficient to trigger an allergic reaction in a small number of individuals.

Similar encephalitides are seen as rare sequelae to the acute stage of infection in mumps, varicella and rubella.

Guillain-Barré syndrome

Similar experiments to those described in the production of EAE, but using peripheral nerve as the immunogen, have resulted in allergic polyneuritis (experimental allergic polyneuritis, EAP). This serves as a model for a rare sequel to certain viral conditions known as the Guillain-Barré syndrome (inflammatory polyradiculopathy). Demyelination of the peripheral nervous system is accompanied by mononuclear cell infiltration and inflammatory changes. The symptoms develop a few days after the acute phase of an infection and range from minor neuropathy with paraesthesiae and weakness to rapidly progressive ascending paralysis and occasionally death. Treatment is supportive including cardiopulmonary support when necessary. Recovery is usual but may be protracted with relapses. Guillain-Barré syndrome has been associated with measles, rubella, varicella-zoster and mumps virus infections. In 1976, the syndrome was associated with an incorporation of swine influenza antigens in the currently available influenza vaccines.

Slow virus diseases

This term has been applied to a collection of persistent infections of the nervous system which are characterized by a long incubation period followed by a degenerative illness which is usually subacute or chronic in nature and usually shortens the life of the host. This unsatisfactory definition encompasses the retroviral disease of sheep, visna, the spongiform encephalopathies, scrapie, kuru, Creutzfeldt–

Jakob syndrome the late manifestation of measles infection, subacute sclerosing panencephalitis and the papovavirus condition, progressive multifocal leucoencephalopathy.

Visna

Visna virus is a member of the lentivirus subfamily of the Retroviridae. It causes two distinct conditions in sheep, visna, which is a progressive and ultimately fatal demyelinating disease of the nervous system and maedi, progressive pneumonia. The clinical picture of the resulting infection appears to be governed by the host response rather than by variation in the virus itself. The incubation period varies from several months to years. Although this virus produces reverse transcriptase and is integrated into the cells of the host it has not been associated with malignant transformation. In addition to the disease processes in the brain and lungs the virus also invades the reticuloendothelial system and thus produces immunosuppression. It is of interest and importance that, at the time of writing, the AIDS virus (HIV) has been classified as a lentivirus (see Chapter 16). Infected sheep develop antibodies to the virus and these can be detected in the CSF as well as the blood of animals with encephalopathy.

Spongiform encephalopathies

During the last two decades a group of nervous system degenerations called the subacute spongiform encephalopathies (from their histopathological effects) has been described and, to an extent, characterized. These agents have most unusual physical and chemical properties and they have no morphological resemblance to any known viruses. Indeed, the apparent absence of nucleic acid in a group of agents that are known to be transmissible suggests the existence of another type of replicative molecule. In the absence of a clear understanding of their nature and because of their similarity to slow virus infections caused by recognized viruses they are included in this chapter. Their incubation periods vary from several months to years and the protracted diseases are invariably fatal. Apart from a transient period of immunosuppression during the incubation period, the pathology is confined to the central nervous system. Neuronal loss is accompanied by spongiform change and astroglial proliferation. Electron microscopy of material from infected brains reveals the presence of proteinaceous structures called prions. Neither cellular nor humoral immunity develops in natural or experimental infections and there is no detectable interferon response.

The unusual nature of the spongiform encephalopathy agents is best illustrated by describing their physico-chemical characteristics. They are resistant to boiling and there is doubt as to whether the normal autoclaving conditions will produce total inactivation. For this reason, specified high temperature autoclaving cycles have been recommended for instruments used on patients with Creutzfeldt–Jakob syndrome. The agents can survive for years in formaldehyde at concentrations used for fixing tissues, they are resistant to many common disinfectants including β-propiolactone, alcohols and phenolics, and are unaffected by proteases and nucleases. The absence of nucleic acid in the infectious particle is confirmed by extreme resistance to ionizing radiation. They appear to be inactivated by 5% hypochlorite and 1N sodium hydroxide.

Scrapie

Scrapie is a natural disease of sheep which has been adapted to grow in mice and other laboratory animals. In sheep, it behaves as a recessive genetic trait and there are considerable differences in susceptibility between different breeds. The name is derived from the clinical effects of the cerebral degeneration on the animal in inducing intense itching and the sheep rub themselves against fences and other objects to try and relieve the sensation. Transmission of scrapie to mice has resulted in a reduction of the incubation periods and this facilitates transmission studies. Mice also show differences in their genetic susceptibility and the incubation period is also dependent on the inoculum size. The long incubation period is probably due to the slow replication rate of the agent and the infectivity level has been shown to increase with the increase in the cell population. At the end stages of the illness the animal develops progressive paralysis and this leads to coma and death.

Transmissible mink encephalopathy

This condition of mink is similar in clinical picture and pathological changes to scrapie in sheep. The agent is very similar to the scrapie agent.

Kuru

Kuru is a subacute, progressive disease of the central nervous system that has been confined to the Fore people who occupy the Eastern Highlands of New Guinea. In the local dialect, kuru means 'to tremble with fear' and the symptoms and signs are ataxia, spasticity and increased reflexes with progression to impaired consciousness and death. Mental alertness is unaffected until the late stages but progressive starvation contributes to the physical deterioration. Epidemiological studies indicate that most cases of the disease occur in adult women and children of either sex. The disease has rarely been seen outside of the area and visitors to the region have not been affected. Inoculation of brain tissue from victims of the disease into primates resulted in similar neurologic effects and pathologic changes to those found in humans after an incubation period of approximately 40 months.

Transmission was found to be related to ritual cannibalism, a practice conducted by the Fore Highlanders as a mark of respect to their deceased relatives. This involved the handling and ingestion of the organs and tissues of the bodies and in view of the highest incidence of the disease in women and children, it is of interest to note that they received the 'offal' including the brain and spinal cord, while the men consumed the muscle tissues. With the abolition of ritual cannibalism in New Guinea the disease has now virtually disappeared.

Creutzfeldt–Jakob syndrome

Creutzfeldt–Jakob syndrome is a rare (one case per million per year) progressive disease of the nervous system, caused by an agent similar in nature to that of Kuru and related to the other agents of spongiform encephalopathy. Unlike Kuru it is found worldwide and it is recognized as a rare cause of presenile dementia. The early effects of forgetfulness, disorientation and frank dementia may lead to psychiatric consultation. The disease progresses to produce changes in gait, increased tone in the limbs and eventually involuntary movements and seizures with eventual coma and death. Following experimental transmission to primates, the agent has now been adapted to grow in mice and guinea pigs. Most cases are sporadic although 20% occur in family members of affected individuals. There is no evidence that the virus has been transmitted by casual contact. Nosocomial infections have occurred following corneal transplantation from an infected individual and via electrodes applied directly to the brain during neurosurgery. In these cases the incubation period was 15–20 months.

Subacute sclerosing panencephalitis (SSPE)

This disease results from chronic measles virus infection of the central nervous system which usually occurs in prepubertal children. It presents in an insidious manner with personality changes, declining intellectual ability and reversion to a more childish behaviour pattern. At this stage the child is often referred to a child psychologist. Motor abnormalities including myoclonic jerks, spasticity, tremors and loss of coordination develop and the child eventually becomes stuporose with difficulties in temperature regulation and cortical blindness. The disease produces a characteristic appearance of bursts of high voltage, slow wave activity, on the electroencephalogram. Death occurs from inanition, superinfection and metabolic disturbances. Although measles antigens can be found in many tissues, most of the pathology is localized to the central nervous system and retina. There is widespread destruction of grey and white matter with intranuclear and intracytoplasmic inclusions in neuronal and oligodendroglial cells together with mononuclear cell infiltrations. The role of measles virus is confirmed by elevated antibody levels including measles-specific IgM in the CSF, the presence of paramyxovirus inclusions in the brain, measles antigen in brain tissue and isolation of the virus from brain and lymph nodes by co-cultivation techniques. The reason for the persistence of virus in sufferers of SSPE may be due to their inability to respond immunologically to the M (matrix) protein of measles. This internal membrane protein is one of six major proteins of the virus and has a key role in virus assembly beneath the cytoplasmic membrane before budding occurs. As infection progresses in the central nervous system the M protein tends to disappear and this may lead to lack of virus assembly and release and hence a defective immunologic response.

SSPE has been particularly associated with measles occurring early in life and usually before the age of 18 months. Its incidence in the United States has declined dramatically as a result of the widespread use of measles vaccine. A similar condition may result from persistence of rubella virus in the nervous system and this is most often seen in adolescents who have recovered from congenital rubella. Rubella virus has been recovered from the brain by co-cultivation.

Progressive multifocal leucoencephalopathy (PML)

PML presents as a dementia in individuals with severe immunocompromise in particular those with disseminated malignancy or AIDS. The early effects of memory impairment, confusion and disorientation are later followed by multiple symptoms and signs including hemiparesis, incoordination, visual abnormalities and seizures. Death usually results within 3–6 months of the onset of disease. In the brain, foci of demyelination are surrounded by giant astrocytes containing intranuclear inclusions. On electron microscopy, these inclusions are found to contain pseudo-crystalline arrays of papovavirus particles and papovavirus antigens are demonstrable in the brain. Two types of papovavirus have been isolated from the brain of patients with PML; one is related to the primate virus SV40, and the other is the human polyomavirus called JC after the initials of the patient from whom it was first isolated. Antibodies to JC virus have been found in about 70% of the population and, although it seems to be an asymptomatic infection in those with normal immunity, it appears to be reactivated and accumulate in the brains of some immunocompromised individuals.

Further reading

Gadjusek D. C. (1977) Unconventional viruses and the origin and disappearance of kuru. *Science*, **197**, 943–60.

Hattwick M. A. W. (1974) Human rabies. *Public Health Rev*, **3**, 229–74.

Johnson K. M. (1979) Arthropod-borne viral fevers. In: *Cecil Textbook of Medicine*, Beeson P. B. *et al.* (Eds). W. B. Saunders, Philadelphia.

Vinken P. J. and Bruyn G. W. (1978) *Handbook of Clinical Neurology: Infections of the Nervous System*, Part 2, Vol. 34. North Holland, Amsterdam.

Chapter 13
Gastroenteritis

Gastroenteritis is a common illness that occurs throughout the year, in epidemic and sporadic form, in all countries. Infants and children, who are naturally less resilient than adults to fluid and electrolyte loss, are most severely affected. It is a major cause of death in children who are malnourished. A variety of infectious agents are responsible and, overall, approximately 20–25% of cases are attributed to bacteria and protozoa. Viruses are considered to be responsible for many of the remainder but investigation has been hampered by our failure to cultivate many of the enteric viruses in the laboratory. Several of the common viruses that are known to replicate primarily in the gut, such as enteroviruses and adenoviruses, have not been firmly established as significant causes of gastrointestinal disease. For many years, the importance of viruses in producing diarrhoeal illness was suspected from the lack of evidence of other aetiological agents in many outbreaks; thus viral gastroenteritis was mainly a diagnosis by exclusion. The fact that viruses could be responsible was confirmed by volunteer studies in which cell-free extracts of diarrhoeal stools were found to reproduce disease when administered orally. The electron microscope has played an important role in the identification and diagnosis of gastroenteritis viruses and, in recent years, several types of virus have been confirmed (or strongly suspected) as primary pathogens. Faecal samples usually contain virus-like particles and problems arise in attempting to assess the significance of these structures to the patient. If a virus is responsible for the symptoms it is usually present in large numbers in the stools and is by far the predominant particle visible by direct electron microscopy. However, to be certain that it is pathogenic it must be present significantly more often in those with symptoms than in matched controls and, in addition to this, other criteria must be satisfied. Seroconversion should be demonstrated in the patient's blood; if the virus cannot be cultured this may be achieved by immune-electronmicroscopy. Other causes of gastroenteritis must be excluded and the virus should be shown to reproduce the disease by experimental administration to another host. Two groups of viruses have satisfied these criteria and are known as the Norwalk agents and rotaviruses. Others are implicated but the final proof is lacking.

Norwalk agents

This is a heterogeneous collection of viruses (27–30 nm diameter) that have been associated with outbreaks of gastroenteritis in people of all ages. They are only partially characterized due to lack of suitable culture systems and their true nature (including their nucleic acid composition) is in doubt. Morphologically, they resemble the parvoviruses and hepatitis A virus (a picornavirus) and they are often referred to as parvo/picornaviruses. The structure of the original Norwalk agent resembles that of a calicivirus. They appear to be very hardy and resistant to acid, ether and exposure to heat and cold. Several different, and distinct, serotypes have been demonstrated by immune-electronmicroscopy. They are known by a variety of names that indicate the source or geographical location of an outbreak, e.g. Norwalk agent, Hawaii agent, Montgomery County agent, Cockle agent. Transmission has been related to consumption of contaminated shell fish and drinking water and outbreaks have resulted from inadequately chlorinated swimming pools. Person–to–person spread occurs during epidemics.

Norwalk virus

Volunteer studies confirmed the pathogenic nature of this virus which was first seen by immune electronmicroscopy in the stool of an adult who had been infected experimentally. Pure extracts of the virus, when given orally, produce acute gastroenteritis in 50% of adult recipients after an incubation period of 24–48 hours. The symptoms of diarrhoea, fever, nausea and vomiting, last for 24–48 hours and virus can be found in the stools for 72 hours after the onset of symptoms. Seroconversion occurs during the course of infection and epidemiological studies have shown that the agent is distributed throughout the world. At least 50% of adults have antibody to the Norwalk virus.

Rotaviruses

Human rotaviruses were first described by Bishop *et al.* in 1973 in the epithelial cells of the duodenal mucosa obtained by biopsy from children with acute gastroenteritis. Similar particles were seen in the faeces and it is surprising, in retrospect, that these viruses, which are normally present in enormous numbers in the stools of infected children, were not recognized before that time. Since then they have been found throughout the world and are believed to account for 40–60% of acute gastroenteritis occurring in children under the age of two years.

Rotaviruses are members of the Reoviridae and are naked spherical particles 65–75 nm in diameter. The name is derived from the Latin word rota (wheel) and describes the electron microscopical appearance of the outer capsid margin as the rim of a wheel surrounding radiating spokes from the inner core. The double-stranded RNA genome is in 11 segments and the virions contain an RNA-dependent RNA polymerase. The rotavirus genus includes a number of similar viruses that cause diarrhoea in birds and mammals (including calves, pigs, lambs, foals, mice and rabbits), and although these viruses are morphologically identical to human rotavirus, they are antigenically distinct.

Antibodies are present in 60–90% of children and most adults have circulating IgG to rotaviruses. Reinfection can occur despite high levels of humoral immunity, however, and local immunity in the gut is probably more significant in terms of protection. Human rotaviruses have been classified into two subgroups on the basis of internal antigens and there are at least four serotypes detectable by differences in surface antigens. Sequential infections with different subtypes have been recorded in children. There is no information on the possibility of cross protection between antibodies to the different subtypes.

Rotaviruses cause disease in all age groups but most severe outbreaks occur in neonates and young children. Many babies become infected during the first few weeks of life particularly while they are in hospital nurseries. Severe diarrhoea may result but many other babies have asymptomatic infection. Infection at this age is modified by the presence of transplacentally acquired antibody and from antibody in colostrum and breast milk. Shedding of virus in the faeces commences during the incubation period and, although seroconversion is uncommon at this age, the development of intestinal immunity is likely from the knowledge that post-neonatal infection produces less severe disease in those who have had a neonatal infection. In children between the ages of three months and five years rotaviruses account for approximately half the hospital admissions necessary for acute gastroenteritis. In tropical countries the incidence of disease is similar throughout the year while in temperate climates most infections occur during the winter months. The incubation period is 24–48 hours, and there is usually an abrupt onset of vomiting followed within hours by copious amounts of watery brown stools. A low grade fever is usually present and symptoms may persist for seven days during which time the child continues to shed virus. Seroconversion occurs in infants and older children. Nosocomial infection is common in children admitted to hospital for other reasons.

In older children and adults asymptomatic infections appear to be relatively common but although outbreaks of disease have been reported in all age groups they are rare.

Other possible viral aetiologies

A number of viral particles have been associated with diarrhoeal outbreaks and some may prove to be pathogenic if they can be shown to satisfy Koch's postulates.

Adenoviruses

Adenoviruses that cannot be cultured by standard techniques are occasionally seen by electron microscopy in children with gastroenteritis and in nosocomial outbreaks, and their presence is significantly more frequent than in matched, disease-free controls. The presence of these viruses in faeces correlates with the time course of the disease process.

Astroviruses

Astroviruses (28–30 nm) have a star-like appearance and have been associated with mild diarrhoea in the newborn and with nosocomial infections. Adult volunteers developed diarrhoea and seroconversion after oral administration and seroprevalence studies have shown that 75% of the adult population of the United Kingdom has circulating antibodies.

Their global significance is unknown.

Coronaviruses

Coronaviruses are known to be intestinal pathogens in dogs, pigs and calves and particles with a similar morphology have been seen in the faeces of humans with acute gastroenteritis. Further evidence is required to assess their aetiological significance.

Pathogenesis and pathology

Similar pathological processes are initiated by all the known gastroenteritis viruses; they produce non-specific and reversible inflammation in the gut mucosa. The viruses replicate in epithelial cells lining the villi in the small intestine and produce vacuolation of the endoplasmic reticulum, swollen mitochondria, increased numbers of lysosomes and multivesicular bodies. The cells undergo lysis and leave the villi denuded and covered with immature cells that have migrated from the crypts. Denuding of the villi allows leakage of fluid and electrolytes into the gut lumen and this probably accounts for the onset of diarrhoea. Contraction of the denuded villi and replacement of mature epithelial cells by immature cells lacking in enzymatic capacity probably amplifies the diarrhoea by decreasing the absorptive capacity and reducing the activity of disaccharidases and other enzymes in the brush border. Glucose-coupled sodium transport is decreased during viral enteritis whereas it is largely unaffected in enterotoxic bacterial infections. Although some children have a degree of inflammation of the gastric and rectal mucosa, the replication of viral pathogens seems to be confined to the small intestine. The intestinal villi appear shortened and the lamina propria is infiltrated with mononuclear cells and polymorphs. The intestinal mucosa has normally recovered completely within 3–4 weeks of the onset of symptoms although some young children suffer persistent histological damage and depression of disaccharidase levels which may cause sugar intolerance. Viraemia has not been recorded in the normally immune but may be present in the immunocompromised.

Clinical effects

The symptoms of viral gastroenteritis have an acute onset and include watery diarrhoea, abdominal colic, fever, nausea and vomiting. Nausea, vomiting and fever often precede the onset of diarrhoea. Blood in the faeces is rare. Upper respiratory symptoms sometimes accompany the gastrointestinal disease. The major importance of these infections lies in their complications resulting from water and electrolyte loss in infants and children under the age of five years. Older children and adults are normally able to withstand these effects. Clinically, dehydration may be detected by dryness of the mucous membranes, sunken eyes, poor peripheral circulation and depression of the fontanelles. Skin elasticity is lost and if the skin is pinched up it does not immediately spring back into place. The child may be irritable or lethargic and if treatment is not available, convulsions due to hypernatraemia may develop. If fluid and electrolyte replacement is not instituted death may result from dehydration and electrolyte imbalance. The mortality in children with pre-existing malnutrition may be as high as 30% and it has been estimated that 350 000 individuals may die from viral gastroenteritis each year in India alone. In malnourished children, further weight loss results from the anorexia and reduced food intake and the viral infection may contribute seriously to growth retardation.

Laboratory diagnosis

Technological advances are leading to new techniques which should improve the diagnosis of viral gastroenteritis but, at the time of writing, these are mainly directed towards the detection of rotaviruses. The electron microscope remains the only method of diagnosing the other established or suspected causative viruses. Fluid faeces may be examined directly after staining with sodium phosphotungstate or ammonium molybdate and the viruses may be identified by their morphology or by immune-electronmicroscopy. Rotavirus infections may also be diagnosed using counter-immunoelectroosmophoresis, ELISA and RIA tests for antigen in faeces and also by detection of rotavirus RNA using hybridization probes (dot-blotting).

Using a rotavirus extract as the antigen, ELISA systems for the detection and quantitation of circulating antibody and specific IgM have been developed. Immune-electronmicroscopy is used to detect antibody to viruses in the Norwalk group.

Prevention and treatment

Improvement in sanitation and water supplies is a major factor in the prevention of spread of these, and many other, enteric infections. In developing countries the passively acquired antibody transferred by breast feeding may be a vitally important defence against the clinical effects of viral gastroenteritis in early life. Nosocomial infection is difficult to control by isolation or cohorting in view of the presence of viral shedding before the onset of disease but particular care should be taken to ensure a high level of hygiene with careful attention to handwashing between attending to patients. No specific antiviral agents are available for treating patients with viral gastroenteritis. Antidiarrhoeal and antispasmodic preparations are of little value and may be dangerous in young children but there is sometimes benefit from antiemetics in older individuals when vomiting is a predominant feature. The main approach to therapy is rehydration and this should be started by mouth as soon as possible. Well-nourished children in developed countries should be given isotonic carbohydrate solutions such as glucose or soft drinks which have been decarbonated. Care should be taken to avoid excess sodium intake as this may contribute to the development of hypernatraemia. In developing countries, oral rehydration is commenced with Oralyte (UNICEF), which contains $NaCl$, $NaHCO_3$, KCl and glucose. If severe dehydration ensues, intravenous fluid and electrolyte replacement is urgently required and if this is correctly applied oral fluids can usually be reintroduced within 24–48 hours.

Further reading

Blacklow N. R. and Cukor G. (1981) Viral gastroenteritis. *New Engl J Med*, **304**, 397–406.

Yolken R. H. and Kapikian J. E. (1979) Rotavirus. In: *Principles and Practice of Infectious Diseases*, Mandell G. L., Douglas R. G. and Bennett J. E. (Eds). John Wiley, New York.

Chapter 14
Viral Hepatitis

Hepatitis (inflammation of the liver) is caused by many different agents, including viruses, bacteria, protozoa, drugs and toxins. A number of different viruses may cause liver cell damage as part of a systemic viral infection e.g. Epstein–Barr virus, cytomegalovirus, yellow fever virus and rubella (acquired *in utero*). The term viral hepatitis is reserved for infections in which the liver is the main target for viral replication and the site of maximal damage; these are hepatitis A, hepatitis B and an ill-defined collection of agents causing non-A non-B hepatitis. Any agents that damage the liver can produce a similar clinical effect and a specific diagnosis can often be obtained only by assessing information from each of the following areas:

1 Epidemiological studies.
2 The patient's history and possible contacts.
3 Specific laboratory tests.
4 Liver biopsy.
5 Long term effects of the infection.

As with some other human virus infections, research in hepatitis has been handicapped by the lack of suitable culture systems for propagation of the viruses. This was largely overcome with hepatitis A and hepatitis B by obtaining large amounts of virus from infected individuals and from higher primates infected experimentally. Following purification procedures, the viruses could be characterized and, with the advent of genetic manipulation, it has been possible to clone specific viral proteins which can be used in diagnostic tests and for vaccine production.

Hepatitis A

Hepatitis A virus is a naked icosahedral virus (27 nm diameter) which contains single-stranded RNA. It is resistant to ether and low pH and a classified as a Picornavirus. Only one serotype has been demonstrated and although, initially, the virus could only be propagated in chimpanzees and marmosets, productive infection has been established in primary marmoset liver cell cultures and in a fetal rhesus kidney cell line. These culture systems are not, however, available in most diagnostic laboratories.

Pathogenesis

Hepatitis A virus has many of the characteristics of an enterovirus and, despite its tropism for the liver, maximal titres of virus are present in the intestines. Viral particles can be visualized in faeces by electron microscopy for 10–14 days before the onset of symptoms and, as the disease develops, their numbers rapidly decrease. Following the phase of replication in the intestines there is a period of viraemia with transfer of the virus to the liver. Replication in liver parenchymal cells results in necrosis and there is an inflammatory reaction with infiltration of lymphocytes and macrophages. The severity of the disease is determined by the extent of liver cell damage and there may be associated biliary stasis. Regeneration occurs at an early stage and, except for those who succumb to massive necrosis, all patients recover completely; although some may have abnormally high transaminase levels for several months, hepatitis A virus does not induce chronic aggressive hepatitis.

Immune response

Antibody develops early in the course of the illness and while the virus is still present in the faeces. There is a classical primary immune response and the early antibody is predominantly of the IgM class. This is replaced by IgG during convalescence and hepatitis A virus specific IgG persists for many years and probably for life. Following recovery the individual is immune to reinfection with hepatitis A virus but as hepatitis may be caused by other, totally unrelated viruses, there is obviously no cross-protection. The sequence of events following hepatitis A virus infection is illustrated in Fig. 14.1.

Epidemiology

Hepatitis A virus is a faecal–oral pathogen and, as with other enteric infections, transmission is associated particularly with faecal contamination of drinking water and food. Shellfish obtained from water that contains human sewage are a common source of hepatitis A and adequate boiling is essential to inactivate any virus that may be present. Outbreaks have been traced to poor hygiene in food handlers

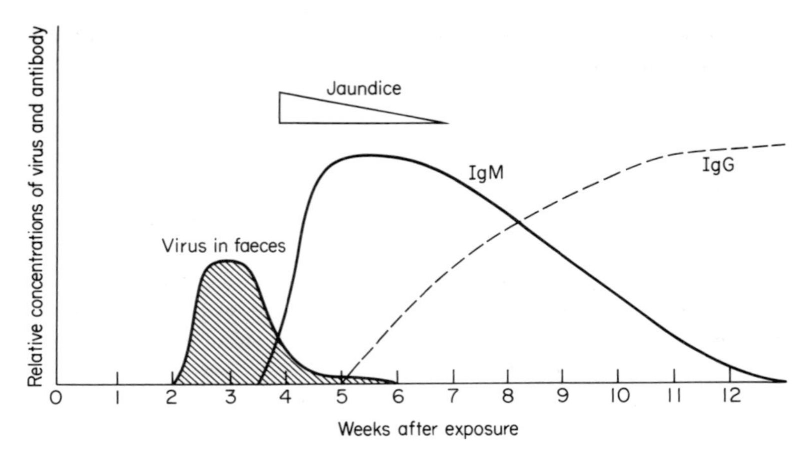

Fig. 14.1 Hepatitis A, typical sequence of events following infection.

and, as there is no carrier state with this virus, the workers involved must have had asymptomatic or mild infections. Person-to-person spread may occur, particularly in overcrowded conditions or if hygiene is poor, and hepatitis A is common in institutions for the mentally handicapped. Seroprevalence studies have shown that infection is highest in developing countries where more than 90% of adults may have antibody. Until recently, about 50% of young adults in England had evidence of past infection but this has been decreasing steadily over the last decade. This indicates that the infection is becoming rarer in children, probably due to better sanitation. It also means, however, that the pool of susceptible adults is enlarging. Asymptomatic infection is very common in children but less so in adults and the latter, if non-immune, are in danger of developing acute hepatitis during visits to endemic areas.

Clinical effects

Many infections with hepatitis A virus are asymptomatic, particularly in childhood, and seroconversion without symptoms, or only mild disease, is probably more common than overt hepatitis at any age. Sporadic cases usually present with jaundice and careful history taking may reveal the likely source of the infection. The incubation period is usually about 30 days (range 14–50 days) and the illness commences with a prodrome in which fever, anorexia, nausea and pain in the right hypochondrium are prominent features. An early sign at this stage of the illness may be a distaste for tobacco in habitual smokers. Jaundice develops after several days and this is accompanied by darkening of the urine and production of clay-coloured stools. The temperature returns to normal as the jaundice develops. The liver is enlarged and tender and serum transaminases, alkaline phosphatase and bilirubin levels are elevated as a result of the liver damage. As the liver recovers, the jaundice fades and normal health is restored. Acute hepatic failure, which may result from widespread liver cell necrosis at the acute stage, is a rare complication of infection.

Laboratory diagnosis

The diagnosis may be suspected from the clinical presentation or from the finding of abnormal liver function tests during the investigation of a non-specific illness. The most common approach to diagnosis is to demonstrate the presence of hepatitis A specific IgM in the patient's serum at the acute phase of the illness. This can be achieved by the use of immunoassays (ELISA or RIA) that are now in routine use. Detection of specific IgG is of considerable value in determining the immune status of individuals particularly in the context of administering protective immunoglobulin for foreign travel (see below). Direct observation of viral particles in the patient's faeces by electron microscopy is rarely of diagnostic value as the virus has usually been eliminated by the time of clinical presentation.

Prevention and treatment

Careful attention to personal hygiene is an important aspect of preventing transmission in the home and in institutions. Individuals should be made aware of the dangers from ingestion of food and water that may have become contaminated with the virus in endemic areas. Shellfish in particular should be viewed with suspicion unless there is reasonable certainty that they come from unpolluted waters or that they have been adequately cooked. Human normal immunoglobulin (HNIG) can be used to protect people in contact with cases of hepatitis A (see Chapter 5) and this is often administered to household contacts. It is also used for the protection of travellers proposing to visit endemic areas and the need for prophylaxis can be assessed by antibody testing. No specific treatment exists for hepatitis A infection and the principles of management rest in supportive therapy with bed rest and adequate nutrition.

Hepatitis B

Hepatitis B virus is the only human representative of a family of DNA viruses (Hepadnaviridae) of which related viruses have been found in woodchucks, Peking ducks and ground squirrels. The complete virion (HBV, Dane particle) is 42 nm in diameter and the spherical structure contains an icosahedral core which is surrounded by a proteinaceous coat. The core contains the viral DNA, DNA polymerase, the core antigen (HBcAg) and the e antigen (HBeAg), a component of the core antigen. The coat of the virion is composed of the surface antigen (HBsAg, Australia antigen) and a feature of infection with this virus is the production of enormous amounts of surplus coat material that

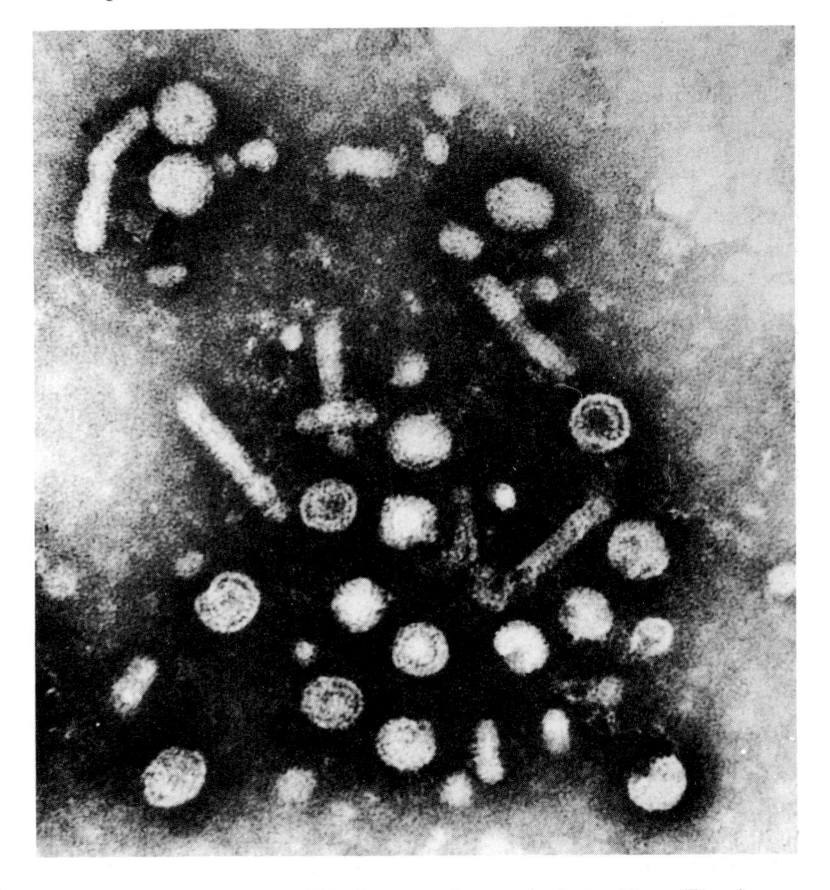

Fig. 14.2 Hepatitis B virus. The electron micrograph shows 42 nm (Dane) particles and the viral subunit structures (20 nm spheres and tubes).

is present in circulation in the form of non-infectious particles; 22 nm spheres and filaments of variable length and 22 nm width. The three particles found in hepatitis B are illustrated in Fig. 14.2. The viral coat (HBsAg) has a group specific antigen a, and two sets of mutually exclusive subtype determinants , d and y and w and r. Thus there are four separate subtypes of hepatitis B virus: adw, adr, ayw and ayr. There is geographical variation in the distribution of these subtypes and the differences can be useful in epidemiological studies. Antigenic cross-reactivity occurs between the different subtypes and cross-protection appears to be solid. Naked core particles are found exclusively in hepatocytes and never exist in uncoated form in circulation.

Although the clinical effects may be identical, hepatitis B differs from hepatitis A in several important respects. The virus is primarily blood-borne and is not known to undergo significant replication in a site other than the liver. It persists in some individuals who become long term carriers of the infection and this persistent state may render them highly infectious to others. Continued replication of the virus in the liver may result in chronic active hepatitis, cirrhosis and the development of hepatoma.

Pathogenesis and pathology

Infected hepatocytes are characteristically enlarged and their bulky cytoplasm has a ground-glass appearance. They are found in clumps and by electron microscopy, HBsAg is found to be associated with the endoplasmic reticulum. Naked core particles containing HBcAg are present in the cell nuclei. Due to the large antigenic load present in hepatocytes and in the serum, together with the knowledge that hepatitis B virus infection is much more likely to be asymptomatic or mild in the immunocompromised, it has been hypothesized that the liver injury in acute hepatitis results from immune mechanisms. Necrosis of hepatocytes results in a scattered focal inflammatory response with macrophage and lymphocyte infiltrations together with portal inflammation and endophlebitis of the central veins. In more severe cases, lines of necrosis extend from the portal tracts to the central veins and this often presages chronic hepatitis and cirrhosis. Those who become asymptomatic carriers may either have normal liver histology or may show chronic portal inflammation that is recognized clinically as chronic persistent hepatitis. This normally resolves completely within months or years of the acute infection. Some carriers develop chronic periportal hepatitis which correlates clinically with chronic active hepatitis and continuing patchy necrosis with fibrosis is likely to lead to the major disruption in liver architecture characteristic of cirrhosis. There is a relationship between hepatitis B virus infection, cirrhosis and the development of hepatoma. This is discussed in Chapter 19.

Immune responses

The nomenclature of the various antigens and antibodies in hepatitis B infection is shown in Table 14.1. Towards the end of the incubation period viral particles and the associated antigens appear in circulation and increase in quantities as the illness develops. In addition to abundant amounts of HBsAg the presence of HBeAg and DNA polymerase signify active replication of virus in the liver and correlate with the presence of large numbers of infectious virions. Although HBcAg is present, it is not detectable in serum due to the early development of specific antibody (anti-HBcAg). As the acute infection resolves the majority of patients clear the antigens from circulation and this is followed by the appearance of detectable antibodies to HBeAg and HBsAg. This sequence of events (Fig. 14.3) indicates recovery and immunity to reinfection. Two types of carrier state are recognized from epidemiological studies and from knowledge of serological responses. Persistence in some individuals is related to a protracted period of antigenaemia but although HBsAg persists at a low level, DNA polymerase and HBeAg are eliminated and antibodies

Table 14.1 Hepatitis B nomenclature

HBV	Hepatitis B virus (hepadnavirus) 42 nm—originally called the Dane particle
HBsAg	Hepatitis B surface antigen—exists as 22 nm spheres and tubules. Present on surface of HBV. Originally called Australia antigen
HBcAg	Hepatitis B core antigen. Associated with 27 nm core of the virus
HBeAg	Hepatitis B e antigen. Related to core antigen. Presence in blood correlates with level of infectivity
Anti-HBs	Antibody to HBsAg
Anti-HBc	Antibody to HBcAg
Anti-HBe	Antibody to HBeAg

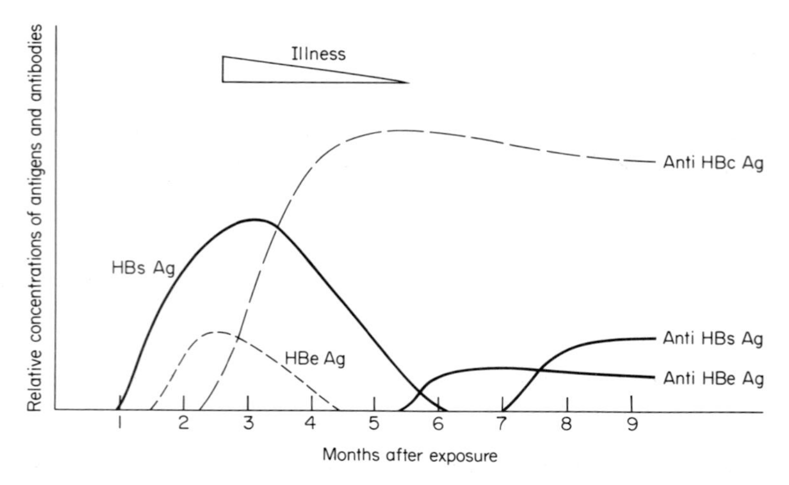

Fig. 14.3 Hepatitis B. Typical sequence of events in an uncomplicated infection with jaundice, complete elimination of the virus and lifelong immunity.

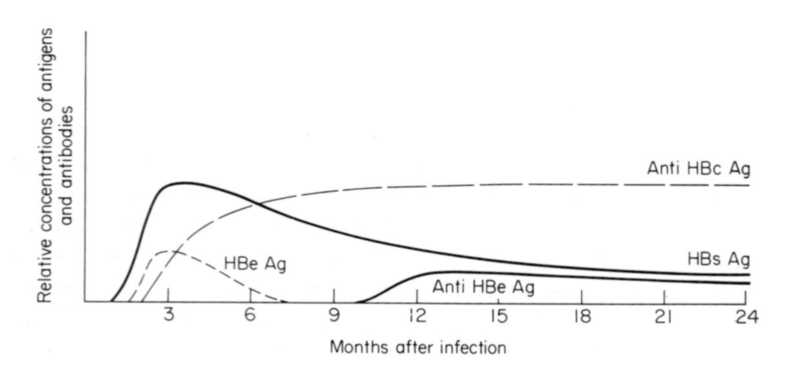

Fig. 14.4 Hepatitis B, showing progression of the acute infection to the low infectivity carrier state with development of antibody to HBeAg.

to HBeAg become detectable. This situation (Fig. 14.4) is favourable to the individual, is compatible with normal liver function and means that there is little or no risk of transmitting the virus to others. The correlation of loss of infectivity with elimination of HBeAg has led to the use of this antigen detection system for determining the potential infectivity of carriers in health care situations. The other type of carrier (Fig. 14.5) remains potentially highly infectious with continued

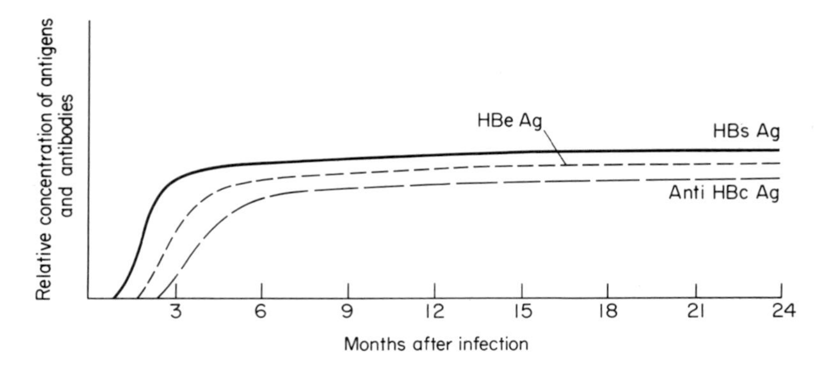

Fig. 14.5 Hepatitis B, showing progression to the infectious carrier state (HBeAg positive).

production of large numbers of circulating virions, high titres of HBsAg and HBeAg, and an absence of detectable antibodies to these antigens. It is this type of carrier who is in danger of chronic liver disease.

Epidemiology

The older names for hepatitis B (serum hepatitis, homologous serum jaundice, hippy hepatitis, etc.) illustrate the association that used to exist between the infection and transfusion of blood and blood products and reuse of syringes. With the development of the transfusion service during World War II, many cases of hepatitis occurred which seemed to be related to transfusion. There had also been a number of recorded instances in which the reuse of needles on successive individuals had led to outbreaks of long incubation hepatitis. Volunteer experiments conducted by McCallum *et al.* in Oxford medical students established the different nature of hepatitis A and hepatitis B in terms of their incubation periods and lack of cross-protection and also demonstrated that hepatitis B could be regularly transmitted by a minute amount of blood or serum (0.0001 ml intradermally). Further human inoculation studies were conducted on mentally retarded children at the Willowbrook State school in New York State where Krugman and colleagues confirmed McCallum's findings and reported that a dose of 0.00004 ml intradermally would consistently produce infection in the non-immune. Studies of cases of acute hepatitis admitted to infectious disease units in the

Western world soon indicated that the vast majority were unrelated to transfusion or the use of contaminated syringes. It became clear that most infections were occurring in young adults and serological studies confirmed the close temporal relationship between acquisition of hepatitis B markers and infection with agents responsible for sexually transmitted diseases such as *Neisseria gonorrhoea, Chlamydia trachomatis* and herpes simplex type 2. Knowledge of the high infectivity demonstrated in the volunteer studies suggested that skin-to-skin contact may be the reason for infections in young adults (and this may indeed be a significant route), but the finding of high titres of antigen in semen and other body fluids supports the likelihood of sexual transmission. Hepatitis B has been found to be particularly common in homosexual men who practise anal intercourse and the trauma associated with this activity, which frequently results in bleeding, is thought to favour the transmission of the virus.

Any technique that allows the transfer of blood or serum from one person to another is potentially likely to transmit hepatitis B. Intravenous drug abusers who share syringes and needles are constantly at risk of infection and are a reservoir of the virus in most communities. Outbreaks have been related to inadequate disinfection of needles and instruments by tattooists, acupuncturists and ear piercers and the risk to health care workers of contracting hepatitis B from inoculation injury with needles used on known carriers has been estimated at 6–20%.

Hepatitis B infection is found worldwide and prevalence rates vary markedly between countries. In some tropical countries as many as 15% of the population are carriers of the virus and it has been estimated that there are 200 million carriers in the world. Mosquitoes and bed bugs have been shown to carry infectious virus but their roles in transmission of infection to humans have not been ascertained.

Hepatitis B does not normally infect the fetus but the baby is at risk of infection during the birth process. The risk is particularly high if the mother has acute hepatitis or if she has circulating HBeAg. Most infants do not develop acute disease but their failure to develop antibodies results in long term carriage. This is a major factor in maintaining the high prevalence of infection in developing countries.

Clinical effects

The incubation period of hepatitis B averages 90 days (range 40–180 days) and the clinical picture is very variable. As with hepatitis A, asymptomatic and minor, atypical infections are common. The commonest presenting feature is jaundice and a minority (<1%) of patients develop fulminant hepatitis with death from acute hepatic failure. The early prodromal symptoms are fatigue, nausea, anorexia and discomfort or pain in the right hypochondrium. The onset of the prodrome and the development of jaundice are usually more gradual than with hepatitis A and the prodrome may be present for 1–3 weeks before jaundice becomes obvious. As with hepatitis A, the fever present during the prodromal illness subsides when jaundice appears. Urticaria and arthritis sometimes precede the jaundice and these are thought to be caused by circulating immune complexes. The jaundice is accompanied by darkening of the urine and clay-coloured stools and it gradually fades as the hepatocellular damage resolves. In children, the onset of symptoms is more abrupt and the icteric phase is shorter. Gastrointestinal effects predominate and vomiting, abdominal pain and ketoacidosis are usual. The prodromal urticaria and arthritis are rare in children but other immune complex phenomena, particularly glomerulonephritis and papular acrodermatitis, are relatively common.

Laboratory diagnosis

A full range of immunoassays (ELISA and RIA) is now commercially available for detecting the antigens and antibodies present in acute hepatitis B and in the carrier state. Reference to Figs. 14.3–14.5 will clarify how these tests may be used for diagnosing a recent infection and for assessing the significance of a positive result. HBsAg detection is used to diagnose acute infection and to screen for the carrier state. HBeAg is used to assess the potential infectivity of carriers and antibodies to the specific antigens indicate past infection and are of value in monitoring progress. An additional test (anti-HBcAg IgM) provides a way of diagnosing recent infection in those who have lost detectable antigen and in whom antibodies have not yet become positive (termed the diagnostic window).

Prevention and treatment

Hepatitis B can be prevented by passive and active prophylaxis. Hepatitis B specific immunoglobulin (HBIG) is prepared from selected donors who have significant anti-HBsAg in their serum. This is given intramuscularly to those who have been exposed to the risk of infection and, depending on the dose, confers protection for 1–3 months. HBIG is used to protect health care personnel who have suffered inoculation injury with sharp instruments or needles used on patients infected with hepatitis B virus. In view of the low dose necessary to establish infection from the most infectious carriers this has been extended to include exposure of skin and mucous membranes to blood. It is also administered to babies born to mothers who have acute hepatitis B or who are HBeAg positive carriers. To ensure that maximal protection is achieved with HBIG, it must be administered within 48 hours of inoculation injury or within 48 hours of birth. A major success in recent years has been the development of a plasma-derived hepatitis B vaccine and this is now commercially available. The raw material is obtained by plasmaphoresis of volunteer HBsAg positive donors and the vaccine consists of highly purified 22 nm particles. The particles are subjected to an extensive inactivation process that has been shown to inactivate all known infectious agents, including the agents of spongiform encephalopathy, and a high level of quality control is maintained. This first generation vaccine has proved to be highly potent and safe after several years of trials and clinical use. Its main limitation, at present, is the cost incurred mainly by its prolonged purification process, which far exceeds the annual per capita allocation for health care in most developing countries. Developments in genetic manipulation have resulted in the introduction of cloned subunit vaccines prepared in yeast cells. These are undergoing field trials at present and it is hoped that this technology, by providing larger amounts of vaccine without the requirement for such stringent safety controls, will reduce the cost of immunization.

There is no specific treatment for acute hepatitis B and bed rest with high calorie diet are important components of supportive care. Some success has been obtained in units specializing in the care of patients with fulminating hepatitis. This has mainly been achieved with intensive care with particular emphasis on the control of cerebral oedema. In addition to this attempts are made to reduce the circulating toxins present as a result of a cessation of liver function by using adsorbant substances such as activated charcoal.

Delta hepatitis

Recently, a new RNA virus called Delta agent has been shown to occur in some individuals with recent or past hepatitis B infection. Delta agent is composed of an RNA core surrounded by HBsAg and it was first described by Rizetto in Italian drug abusers and recipients of multiple transfusions. Since then infection has been reported from other parts of the world. Infection is dependent on hepatitis B replication with synthesis of HBsAg and once Delta infection is established it interferes with the expression of hepatitis B viral gene products and reduces its circulating infectivity markers. The incubation period of Delta hepatitis varies between 2 and 12 weeks and is shorter in those previously infected with hepatitis B than in recipients of a dual infection. In the latter situation the effect of both viruses is likely to result in a particularly severe attack of hepatitis. Delta infection is transmitted by blood transfer in a similar manner to hepatitis B virus. Infection can be diagnosed by antibody immunoassays (IgM and IgG) using antigens derived from infected human liver tissue.

Non-A non-B hepatitis

With the advent of sensitive diagnostic tests for hepatitis B infection and the knowledge that, as it does not produce a carrier state, hepatitis A is rarely blood-borne, virtually all cases of post-transfusion hepatitis are caused by an ill defined collection of viruses termed non-A non-B. Although transmission studies in higher primates have confirmed the existence and communicability of at least two distinct viruses their characterization is awaited. No diagnostic tests are available and the diagnosis can only be achieved on epidemiological grounds and by exclusion of other causes of hepatitis. Non-A non-B hepatitis is usually insidious in onset, mild and anicteric but results in a high incidence of chronic liver disease. Most transmitters of the disease are asymptomatic and thus a chronic carrier state is presumed. In addition to cases occurring after blood transfusion, non-A non-B hepatitis viruses are thought to account for the high prevalence of liver enzyme abnormalities found in haemophiliacs receiving pooled Factor VIII and infection has been recorded in patients undergoing haemodialysis and renal transplantation.

Sporadic non-A non-B hepatitis contributes significantly to the cases of acute hepatitis requiring hospital admission and the observation of repeated attacks in intravenous drug abusers supports the probability that several different viruses are prevalent in the community.

Further reading

Gerety R. J. (1981) *Non-A non-B hepatitis*. Academic Press, New York.

Tiollais P., Pourcel C. and Dejean A. (1985) The hepatitis B virus. *Nature*, 489–95.

Zuckerman A. J. and Howard C. R. (1979) *Hepatitis viruses of man*. Academic Press, London.

Chapter 15
Intra-uterine Infections

Several viruses are known to infect the fetus during the course of systemic infection in the mother. Reference was made earlier (Chapter 10), to the danger to the neonate from transplacentally acquired varicella-zoster infection, and poliomyelitis and neonatal vaccinia infection may be present at, or soon after, birth as a result of intra-uterine infection. Some viral infections are more severe during pregnancy than at other times (e.g. smallpox, hepatitis, poliomyelitis) and these, and some others (e.g. rubella, vaccinia, measles) have been associated with increased fetal mortality. Animal experiments have indicated that artificially raising the body temperature increases the incidence of abnormalities in the offspring. If this is applicable to the human, it may be possible for any pyrexial illness to cause congenital abnormality if it occurs during critical periods of pregnancy. It must be remembered, when considering viral causes of abnormality, that the background rate of abnormalities in babies born to women who have had apparently normal pregnancies, with no evidence of infection, is 2.5%. It is, in fact, remarkable that the majority of women who suffer from significant systemic viral infections, such as varicella, during pregnancy produce totally normal babies.

Four virus infections are known to be potentially teratogenic (Table 15.1). Evidence has been presented that the AIDS virus, HIV, may be a cause of congenital malformation of the nervous system in babies born to infected mothers. These reports are awaiting confirmation.

Rubella and cytomegalovirus, the major causes of congenital abnormality, have two important features in common. Both establish a smouldering, low grade infection in the fetus and, for both viruses, there is a large pool of susceptible women of childbearing age (approximately 10% for rubella, 50% for cytomegalovirus in most western countries).

Table 15.1 Viruses which cause congenital abnormality

Cytomegalovirus
Rubella
Herpes simplex
Varicella-zoster

Rubella

In 1941 the Australian ophthalmologist, Sir Norman Gregg, reported the finding of cataracts in children born to mothers who had had rubella infection during the first trimester of pregnancy. Further studies on these children revealed other forms of ocular defects (e.g. microphthalmia and glaucoma), mental retardation, heart abnormalities and low birth weights with failure to thrive. Other investigators described the development of sensorineural deafness in congenital rubella. In 1964 a major epidemic of rubella swept the USA and left an estimated 30 000 babies with congenital abnormality. This provided further information of the extensive clinical manifestations of intra-uterine infection and prompted a major drive towards the development of effective vaccines.

Pathogenesis and immunology

The features of postnatal rubella were described in Chapter 8. The viraemia accompanying primary infection may lead to transplacental infection. This can occur at any stage of pregnancy with the result that the baby is born with a persisting infection; virus can be isolated for several months (mean nine months) after birth. The fetus is only at significant risk from the primary infection, as the circulating antibody resulting from previous rubella or immunization in the mother prevents viraemia. Rubella virus exerts maximal damage during the early stages of embryogenesis, when the most important structural changes are occurring. Thus, disturbance to normal growth processes from concurrent viral replication during a critical phase such as the rotation of the embryonic heart may result in a grossly malformed organ.

Many of the clinical features of congenital rubella can be explained by the active replication of the virus in fetal tissues. This may produce widespread organ damage, e.g. myocarditis and giant cell hepatitis, or be responsible for focal damage, e.g. cataracts, sensorineural deafness and epilepsy. Persistence of viral replication in the lens and the auditory nerve can result in progressive dysfunction for months, or years, after birth; this is an example of persistence in privileged sites, out of contact with the full impact of immune mechanisms.

Studies of viral replication *in vitro* have revealed the production of soluble antimitotic factors by rubella-infected cells that can slow cell division in uninfected cultures. The nature of these factors has not been defined but interferons, which have growth regulatory properties, are likely candidates. Fetal tissues obtained at 10–12 weeks gestation have been shown to produce interferon in response to rubella infection *in vitro*. In addition, rubella is known to induce chromosomal abnormalities in infected cells. Either, or both, of these effects may account for the clinical evidence of growth retardation seen in congenital rubella. Rubella infected babies have significantly low birth weights despite a normal length gestation period. The commonest cardiac abnormalities (patent ductus arteriosus and septal defects) relate to delays in maturation. Mental retardation may reflect a reduction of cell division in the central nervous system.

In addition to these probable effects on the fetus from direct viral pathogenicity the possibility of immunopathological effects must be remembered. Fetal rubella infection is not an example of immunological tolerance and the fetus mounts a prominent immune response in an attempt to control and eliminate the virus. Immaturity of the immune system delays the final suppression and elimination until months after birth but, at the time of birth, high levels of circulating IgM and IgG are present. This antibody response to high levels of circulating viral antigen is likely to lead to immune complex phenomena that may contribute to the pathogenesis of congenital rubella.

Epidemiology

It is hoped, and expected, that the annual incidence of congenital rubella will be seen to decrease steadily as a result of the introduction of immunization campaigns that commenced in 1969 in the USA and 1970 in the UK. This reduction has been slow to appear in the UK, mainly due to the poor acceptance rate for the vaccines and attempts have been made to increase their uptake by teenage girls and to reduce the pool of susceptibles by testing and immunizing women of childbearing age. The rubella infection rate in pregnancy has been estimated at 1 per 1000 in interepidemic years, rising to 22 per 1000 during epidemics.

Clinical effects

Fetal damage is associated with maternal rubella occurring in the first four months of pregnancy. The incidence of abnormalities is maximal during the first month (50–60%) and decreases as pregnancy continues. The abnormality rate following infections during the first trimester has been recorded as 15–35%. This range of abnormalities obtained from different studies probably reflects the intensity of follow-up of the infants as the more subtle defects, particularly deafness, are often not detectable until several weeks or months after birth. Infection during the first month frequently leads to multiple abnormalities. Maternal rubella in the fourth month of pregnancy carries an abnormality risk of 5%, twice the incidence of defects in uninfected pregnancies. The predominant defect at this stage is deafness. Studies of intra-uterine infection occurring after the fourth month have failed to reveal a significant incidence of abnormality.

The spectrum of clinical effects of intra-uterine rubella is listed in Table 15.2. The probable mechanism of many of these abnormalities has already been discussed. A few additional comments serve to clarify the clinical presentations. Hepatomegaly and hepatosplenomegaly are common features of first trimester infection. Enlargement of the liver alone is found in cardiac failure in association with severe cardiac dysfunction resulting from developmental abnormalities or from myocarditis. Hepatosplenomegaly may result from viral replication in the liver causing a giant cell hepatitis. The effects of the virus in the central nervous system may produce varied effects that can cause serious management problems as the child matures. The resultant meningoencephalitis may cause severe mental retardation or produce a hyperactive child with severe behavioural problems that are difficult to control.

Table 15.2 Fetal abnormalities caused by rubella infection

Organ	Abnormalities
Eye	Cataract, Glaucoma, Microphthalmia
Ear	Sensorineural deafness
Heart	Patent ductus arteriosus, septal defects, major disorders of cardiac organisation including pulmonary stenosis and Fallot's tetralogy, myocarditis.
CNS	Meningoencephalitis, epilepsy, spasticity
Liver	Hepatomegaly—secondary to cardiac failure. Hepatosplenomegaly—if hepatitis present.
Purpura	Thrombocytopenia due to depression of haemopoiesis
Low birth weight	Usually full gestation but significantly low birth weight with perinatal mortality of approximately 20%.
Bones	Areas of rarefaction visible on radiographs.
Immune phenomena often seen at approximately 9 months of postnatal life	
Rash	Similar to that of acquired postnatal rubella
Pneumonitis	Associated with immune complex deposition.

Thrombocytopenia is often present at birth and may be suspected from the presence of purpura. Suppression of haemopoiesis by viral replication appears to cause this phenomenon in the fetus unlike the process of platelet consumption associated with postnatal rubella (Chapter 8). Viral replication in bone marrow is further reflected in the finding of rarefaction of long bones detected by radiological examination.

Late effects of intra-uterine rubella are sometimes noted after approximately nine months of postnatal life. Development of a maculopapular rash, similar to that seen in uncomplicated postnatal rubella, and pneumonitis are thought to be immune complex phenomena related to maturation of the immune responses at a time when elimination of virus is taking place.

Laboratory diagnosis

It has been mentioned, in Chapter 8, that rubella cannot be satisfactorily diagnosed on clinical grounds alone due to the ability of other viral infections to produce similar illnesses. An additional problem in relation to intra-uterine rubella is the fact that asymptomatic infections are common and the fetus is at risk from viraemia that may occur regardless of the clinical status of the mother. Women (and their medical practitioners) should be aware of the dangers of entering pregnancy without rubella antibody, the dangers posed (if seronegative) from close contact with children with rashes and the need to proceed to laboratory testing to ensure that infection, after a possible contact, has not occurred. If rubella infection can be demonstrated in early pregnancy the risks to the fetus, from infection at that stage, should be explained to the prospective parents. A decision can then be made by them in consultation with the obstetrician as to whether the pregnancy should continue or be terminated in the interests of the offspring.

The laboratory tests used in the routine diagnosis of rubella in pregnancy have been described in Chapter 6. Virus isolation is technically difficult and is not normally applied in this situation.

Haemagglutination-inhibiting (HAI) antibody rises at the time of the clinical illness and this provides a specific and sensitive test for current infection. The sequence of events following infection is illustrated in Fig. 15.1. Serum taken during the incubation period (point A) in a susceptible woman will have no detectable HAI antibody, while a significant level of antibody will be present at points B and C

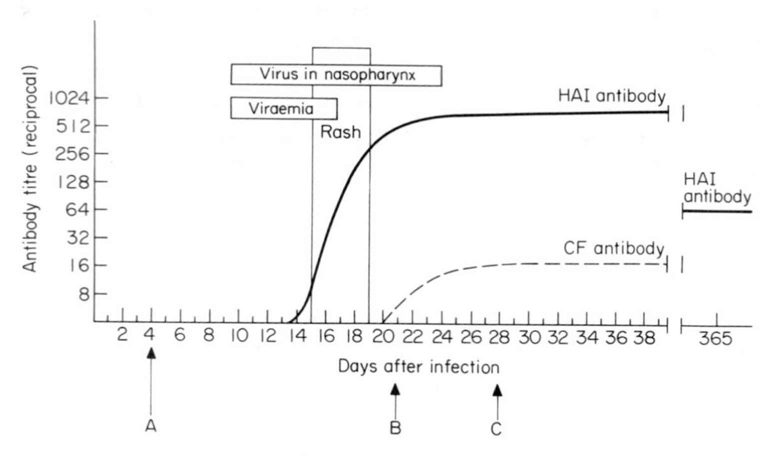

Fig. 15.1 Rubella diagnosis, showing the development of HAI and CFT antibody. See text for reference to the sampling times A, B and C.

(three and four weeks after infection). HAI antibody testing, with convincing evidence of seroconversion, is of major importance in diagnosis providing serum is available within the few days following contact. If the woman presents at point C, the HAI antibody levels may have already reached a plateau and even if they are still rising their quantitation cannot distinguish between primary infection and reinfection. In this situation, detection of rubella specific IgM in the serum will confirm that recent rubella infection has occurred. The relative relationships of IgM and IgG are indicated on Fig. 15.2.

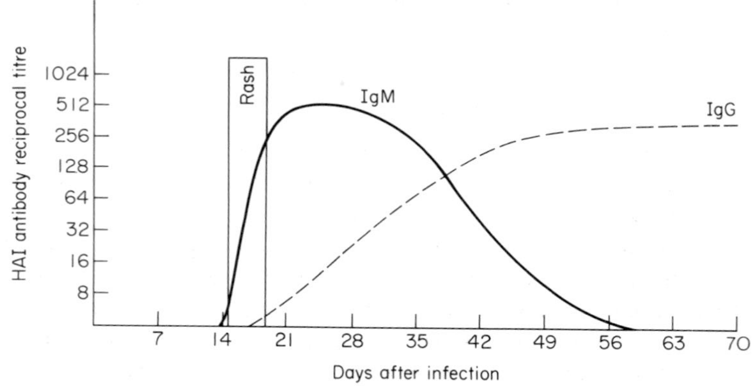

Fig. 15.2 Rubella diagnosis. Typical sequence of specific IgM and IgG responses.

Infection in the newborn infant can be diagnosed most easily by the detection of rubella-specific IgM in cord blood or in circulation. Persistence of rubella-specific IgG for longer than 3–6 months after birth is consistent with intrauterine infection as maternally acquired IgG normally disappears by this time. The high levels of virus produced by the newborn means that virus isolation may be more readily achieved than in older children and adults.

Prevention

The efficacy of currently available rubella vaccines and the lack of benefits from immunoglobulin in attempts at passive prophylaxis have been described in Chapter 8.

Cytomegalovirus

The main characteristics of cytomegalovirus (CMV) infection were described in Chapter 10. The first reports of the association of CMV with a rare, severe disease in neonates come from autopsy reports at the beginning of this century. These effects, termed on the basis of the widespread finding of large inclusion-bearing cells, were known as cytomegalic inclusion disease. An infectious aetiology was suspected, but further definition awaited the isolation of the virus in 1956. Culture of the virus in human embryonic fibroblasts led to the development of diagnostic tests which in turn allowed a clearer definition of the effects of CMV on the fetus, serological studies of the prevalence of infection in the community, and its incidence in pregnancy.

Pathogenesis and immunology

Studies in the USA and UK have indicated that between 0.3 and 1% of infants are infected with CMV at the time of birth. In addition, the high rate of reactivation (12%) of latent virus in late pregnancy, particularly in the region of the cervix, appears to produce infection during the birth process. Reports of congenital abnormalities due to CMV in siblings indicate that, unlike rubella, damage to the fetus may result from recurrent infection in addition to the primary attack. A further difference from rubella infection comes from studies of primary infections in pregnancy. The fetus can be damaged from infection at any stage and in one study in London, most of the damage occurred after the stage when terminations would have been legally acceptable.

The mechanisms involved in the development of the various clinical manifestations are not clearly defined. In severe cytomegalic inclusion disease, the presence of infected cells in many organs suggests widespread replication of the virus that is likely to disturb normal function. Hepatitis, chorioretinitis and progressive sensorineural deafness are probably the result of continuing viral replication. Other conditions present, or developing, in the neonatal period such as pneumonitis may have an immunopathological aetiology. Congenital CMV, like rubella, induces an infection that persists for a long period after birth. Virus may be isolated from the urine for a period of three years and, as with rubella, this probably reflects difficulty in mounting an immune reponse which can finally eliminate virus replication rather than the development of a state of tolerance.

Epidemiology

Retrospective studies of primary CMV infection occurring during pregnancy have indicated that the infection is almost always asymptomatic. Estimates of the numbers of babies born each year in England and Wales who will suffer long term effects of CMV, particularly deafness and cerebral involvement, have been 500–1000. The incidence of severe cytomegalic inclusion disease with disseminated infection involving many different organs is very low (<1 per 10 000 live births). It is not clear at present whether there are geographical differences in the incidence of congenital abnormalities due to CMV. The high prevalence of antibodies present in some developing countries, while reducing to less than 10% the pool of women of childbearing age without antibody, does not seem to result in less congenital abnormality. There may be important cofactors present in some of the areas where epidemiological studies have been conducted (e.g. alcohol and drug abuse) that are less prevalent in other areas.

Clinical effects

The majority of neonates infected *in utero* with CMV have no signs of infection at birth and develop normally with no ill effects from the presence of the virus which may be excreted in their urine in large amounts. The main features of congenital CMV infection are listed in Table 15.3. Of those who show signs of illness, most have minor and self-limiting effects the commonest being hepatomegaly with pro-

Table 15.3 Congenital abnormalities caused by intra-uterine cytomegalovirus infection

CNS	Microcephaly → mental retardation Spasticity, epilepsy Periventricular calcification
Eye	Choroidoretinitis
Ear	Sensorineural deafness
Liver	Hepatosplenomegaly—due to hepatitis. Jaundice is often present
Purpura	Thrombocytopenia due to depression of haemopoiesis
Anaemia	Haemolytic
Pneumonitis	This may develop soon after birth

longed jaundice. Other related disorders, such as thrombocytopenic purpura (due to suppression of the haemopoietic system) and pneumonitis, are usually transient. Cerebral involvement which has been regarded as a major cause of microcephaly may have less obvious effects on intellectual development in early life. Replication of virus within the brain may be detected by the presence of periventricular calcification, detectable on radiographs of the head. The destruction of the retina and auditory epithelium are likely to be progressive and lead to blindness and increasing nerve deafness. In addition to the specific abnormalities induced by CMV, the presence of a potentially immunosuppressive virus may lead to frequent bacterial infections which may contribute to difficulties in early development.

Laboratory diagnosis

This has been described previously (Chapter 10). In view of the fact that virtually all infections in pregnancy are asymptomatic, there is rarely an indication for investigations of possible CMV infection. Screening of pregnant women is not indicated for two main reasons. Many, if not most, of the infections leading to fetal damage occur late in pregnancy in the second and third trimester, and even if one were to identify seroconversion and active infection, the low ratio of disease to infection would probably render intervention unacceptable.

Prevention and treatment

There is little prospect for the development of vaccines to prevent infection with CMV. Early attempts to introduce live vaccines have been abandoned due to concern over potential oncogenicity of herpes viruses. The fact that infection and latency with one strain of the virus may not prevent natural reinfection with different strains hardly generates optimism for effective vaccination. Preliminary trials of a killed vaccine in transplant recipients showed some apparent modification of the symptoms of CMV, but did not prevent infection.

Some hope comes from recent antiviral drug development. One substance, dihydroxypropoxymethyl guanine (DHPG, gancyclovir) has shown benefit in the treatment of severe CMV infection in adults. It has the disadvantage of potentially serious side effects but if safer compounds can be developed, they should be of value in treating the progressive retinitis and sensorineural deafness that occasionally follows intra-uterine CMV infection.

Herpes simplex viruses and varicella-zoster virus

Primary infections with herpes simplex and varicella-zoster viruses have been associated with transplacental infection and congenital abnormality. The similarities in the abnormalities produced in the few reports in the literature indicate that the risks are real. However, the rarity of transmission and the remote danger of congenital abnormality compared to the background rate in uninfected pregnancies, leads most virologists to recommend that pregnancies complicated by primary herpes simplex or varicella should continue. Several reports (<10) in the world literature incriminate herpes simplex infection with the development of congenital malformations of the central nervous system (microcephaly, intracranial calcification, microphthalmia and retinal dysplasia) in association with vesicular skin lesions containing infectious virus. A small number of babies born to mothers who had varicella during pregnancy have had various defects of which the most consistent have been hypoplastic limbs and linear scarring of the skin.

Further reading

Glasgow L. A. and Overall J. C. (1983) Viral and protozoal perinatal infections. In: *Behrman's Neonatal-Perinatal Medicine*, 3rd edition, pp. 692–707. Fanaroff A. A. and Martin R. J. (Eds).

Hanshaw J. B. and Dudgeon J. A. (1978) *Viral Diseases of the Fetus and Newborn*. W. B. Saunders, London.

Hurley R. (1983) Virus infections in pregnancy and the puerperium. In: *Recent Advances in Clinical Virology*, No. 3, pp. 19–55. Waterson A. P. (Ed). Churchill Livingstone, Edinburgh.

Chapter 16
HIV and AIDS

During the 1980s the world has experienced the escalation of an epidemic of infection with an apparently new virus, human immunodeficiency virus (HIV). This virus causes the acquired immune deficiency syndrome (AIDS) and it was previously known as lymphadenopathy virus (LAV) and human T lymphotropic virus type 3 (HTLV-3). HIV establishes persistent infections in the immune system and central nervous system and AIDS and encephalopathy are severe manifestations of a virus that, in the short term, has been seen to produce a spectrum of clinical effects. After seven years of the epidemic, the majority of those infected are asymptomatic and others have other forms of disease including persistent generalized lymphadenopathy (PGL) and thrombocytopenic purpura. The existence of this epidemic was realized in 1981 from the increasing numbers of patients who presented with the opportunistic conditions (Kaposi's sarcoma, *Pneumocystis pneumoniae* pneumonia and other infections) that are the main manifestations of the immunocompromise produced by HIV. At that time, however, the aetiology was unknown and the Centres for Disease Control (CDC), Atlanta, Georgia, introduced the following definition for full-blown AIDS, based on clinical criteria:

> 'A person who has had: 1) a reliably diagnosed disease that is at least moderately indicative of an underlying cellular immune deficiency; but who, at the same time, has had 2) no known cause of cellular immune deficiency nor any cause of reduced resistance reported to be associated with that disease'.

Infants under the age of 28 days and individuals over the age of 60 were excluded from this original definition in view of the difficulties in distinguishing between AIDS and congenital immunodeficiency states and sporadic Kaposi's sarcoma in the elderly. The report of the discovery of the causative virus in 1983 has led to the introduction of diagnostic tests for HIV and together with several years experience in studying the clinical effects of the infection, this has led to the introduction of a classification system for the spectrum of the clinical effects of HIV (see Table 16.1).

Table 16.1 Classification of HIV infection

Group	I	Acute infection
Group	II	Asymptomatic infection
Group	III	Persistent generalized lymphadenopathy
Group	IV	Other disease
	A	Constitutional disease
	B	Neurologic disease
	C	Secondary infectious diseases
	D	Secondary cancers
	E	Other conditions

Human Immunodeficiency Virus (HIV)

HIV is a member of the Retroviridae. The viruses are pleomorphic and enveloped (90–120 nm diameter) and the genome contains duplicate copies of single-stranded RNA, each strand having a molecular weight of approximately 3 million atomic mass units. The particles contain a novel enzyme, reverse transcriptase (RNA-dependent DNA polymerase), which enables the virus to convert its RNA genome into a DNA copy that can then be integrated into the genome of an infected cell. The Retroviridae produce a variety of diseases in many different species of animals (Table 16.2) and the effects of these viruses

Table 16.2 Diseases caused by retroviruses in animals

Disease	Virus(es)	Host
Leukaemia	Rous sarcoma virus	Chicken
Lymphoma	Lymphoid leukosis viruses	Chicken
Carcinoma	Mammary tumour viruses	Mouse
Sarcoma	Simian sarcoma virus	Woolly monkey
Immune deficiency	Feline leukaemia virus	Cat
Wasting	Visna virus	Sheep
Anaemia	Equine infectious anaemia virus	Horse
Abortion	Feline leukaemia virus	Cat
Autoimmunity	Murine leukaemia virus	Mouse
Osteopetrosis	Lymphoid leukosis viruses	Chicken
Pneumonia	Maedi virus	Sheep
Slow neuropathy	Visna virus	Sheep
Arthritis	Caprine arthritis—encephalitis virus	Goat
Acute encephalitis	Caprine arthritis—encephalitis virus	Goat
Paralysis	Moloney leukaemia virus	Mouse
None	Spumavirinae	Several species

in inducing tumour formation, immunocompromise and encephalopathy have been studied by many workers since the beginning of the century. Similarities in morphology, genomic sequence of the polymerase gene and clinical effects between HIV and the slow virus disease of sheep, Visna (see Chapter 12) have led to its classification as a member of the lentivirus subfamily of the Retroviridae. The discovery of human T cell leukaemia virus type 1, HTLV-1 (see Chapter 19), a cause of adult T cell leukaemia, revealed the existence of the first known human retrovirus. This discovery was made possible by two important developments during the 1970s. The first of these was the identification of the enzyme reverse transcriptase; this helped to explain the replication cycle of retroviruses and also provided a method of detecting their presence and quantitating their growth in culture. The second advance was the discovery, characterization and purification of the natural substance T cell growth factor (TCGF, Interleukin 2). TCGF permits the prolonged culture of normal and malignant T lymphocytes and this allows the replication of any retroviruses that may be present, in free or integrated form, within those cells. Thus, with these developments in technology, and the precedent of the isolation of HTLV-1, extensive investigation of material from patients with AIDS and related conditions led to the discovery of the AIDS virus, in a patient with persistent generalized lymphadenopathy, by Barré-Sinoussi and her colleagues in 1983 at the Pasteur Institute in Paris. The significance of this isolation and the association of the virus with AIDS was confirmed in 1984 by workers at the National Cancer Institute in Bethesda, Maryland. Adaptation of the virus to continuous cell lines that were not totally susceptible to the cytocidal effects of the virus allowed the preparation of concentrated, purified stocks of HIV and this led to the successful mapping of the entire genomic structure of several different isolates of the virus. Comparison of genomic maps from isolates obtained at different times and in different areas has revealed considerable base sequence variation. This has occurred throughout the entire genome, but is particularly marked in the envelope gene. The genetic composition of the later North American viruses differs from the first isolates by approximately 10%, and an isolate from central Africa is 25% different. The organisation and coding potential of the genome of HIV is shown in Fig. 16.1. In addition to the three main genes that form the basic structure of retroviruses (gag, pol and env), coding respectively for the internal structural proteins, the reverse transcriptase and the envelope glycoproteins, there are additional coding sequences (art and tat genes) that control viral replication.

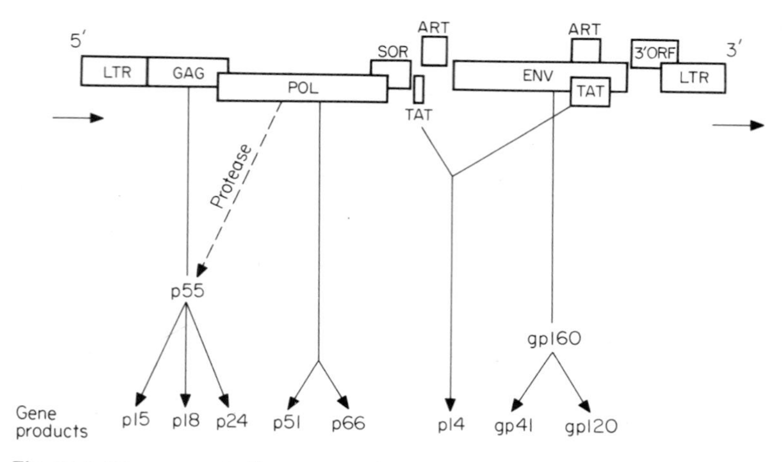

Fig. 16.1 Diagrammatic illustration of the structure and gene products of human immunodeficiency virus (HIV-1).

Pathogenesis

HIV produces widespread and varied effects in its human host as a result of infection, destruction and alteration of function of certain specific target cells. The receptor necessary for attachment of the virus to cells is the OKT4 (CD4) antigen, the marker antigen that is used to identify a subpopulation of T lymphocytes, the helper T cells. This antigen is also expressed on macrophages and other antigen-presenting cells. These cells appear to be the main targets for the virus and the knowledge that blood macrophages are present within the brain, and that there are related antigen-presenting cells in neuroglial tissue, probably explains the growth of virus in brain tissue and resulting encephalopathy.

The sequence of events occurring during HIV replication is shown schematically in Fig. 16.2. After attachment to a permissive cell and fusion of the viral and cellular membranes, the viral RNA is released into the cytoplasm. The particle-associated reverse transcriptase initiates the production of a double stranded DNA copy of the viral genome and this is integrated into the cellular genome as a DNA provirus. Replication of this integrated provirus with the cellular genome results in the production of new viral RNA and proteins and these are assembled in the cytoplasm to produce progeny virus which buds from the plasma membrane. Although HIV has cytocidal properties it appears to be able to establish a long-term productive

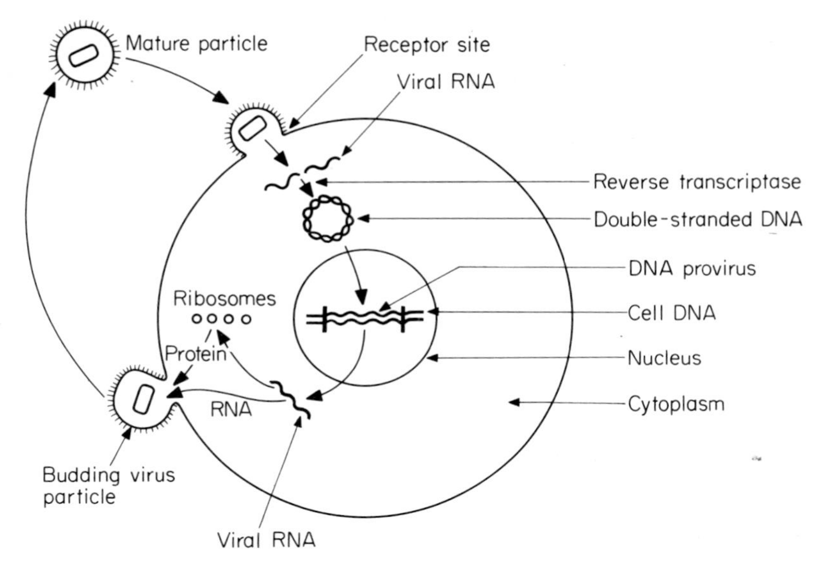

Fig. 16.2 Schematic illustration of the replication process of human immunodeficiency virus (HIV-1).

infection in permissive cells and this results in the establishment of a population of cells that are continually shedding infectious virions. The presence of free virus in circulation stimulates the production of specific antibodies but these have been shown to lack neutralizing capacity and this explains the persistence of infectivity in asymptomatic carriers of the virus.

Progression from asymptomatic carriage of HIV to AIDS has been associated with a depletion in the helper T cell population and with other abnormalities in the numbers of immunocompetent cells and their functions. The extent and significance of these abnormalities have yet to be fully explained, but disturbances of macrophage function, increases in suppressor T cells and polyclonal activation of B lymphocytes, with the important consequences of failure to respond to neo-antigens, are central to the immunocompromise that leads to the development of opportunist conditions. It has been assumed that activation of the immune system in those who are infected with HIV is likely to lead to increased virus production and possibly to increased immune dysfunction and progression to illness. For this reason, avoidance of contact with other infections and adoption of a healthy lifestyle has become a main theme in counselling.

Infection of the brain has been associated with progressive encephalopathy, cerebral atrophy and dementia and this is thought to be caused by destruction of the subcortical white matter and deep grey nuclei with dilatation of ventricles and widening of sulci. The pathogenicity of the virus within the brain requires further investigation. It should be noted that HIV does not possess a viral oncogene and has not been shown to have oncogenic potential. The tumours associated with the infection are similar to those occasionally seen in patients with other causes for immunocompromise and are opportunistic in nature.

Immunology

The profound effects of HIV on the immune system have already been summarized in the previous section. Following infection, there appears to be a variable period (two weeks to at least three months) before the appearance of specific viral markers in the serum. Viral antigen (p24) is the first marker to become detectable; this is present for 1–2 months and disappears with the appearance of antibodies. This switch from antigenaemia to antibody production appears to coincide with the occurrence of a mononucleosis-like illness (fever, lymphadenopathy, rash and arthralgia), experienced by some patients, that is probably immune complex mediated. Laboratory tests have been developed for the detection of two specific antibodies (p24 and gp41) and sequential sampling from HIV positive individuals has revealed the temporal characteristics of these antibodies (see Fig. 16.3). Once developed, antibodies to the envelope glycoprotein appear to persist regardless of the clinical state of the individual. Antibodies to the core protein p24 decline with the onset, or imminent

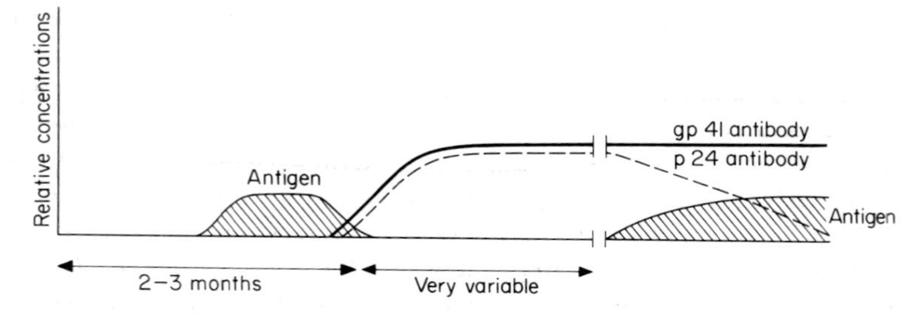

Fig. 16.3 Postulated sequence of antigen and antibody responses following infection with human immunodeficiency virus (HIV-1).

development, of illness and the reduction in p24 antibodies correlates with the reappearance in serum of viral antigen. Thus, quantitation of p24 antigen or antibody in serum appears to be of prognostic value in assessing the significance of HIV infection in an individual.

Preliminary studies suggest that the presence of HIV antigen in the CSF may correlate with active disease within the central nervous system.

Epidemiology

The first cases of AIDS occurred in homosexual men in the United States and investigations of their lifestyles indicated that they had exposed themselves to very large numbers of sexual partners. This led to the early misconceptions that AIDS was a phenomenon of homosexual men and was probably related to a lifestyle factor such as nitrite abuse or infection with an unusual variant of a common infectious disease. When other groups were seen to develop the disease (drug abusers, transfusion recipients, haemophiliacs, sexual partners of people in the other groups and babies born to risk group parents) it became clear that AIDS was a new transmissible virus infection and a threat to everyone. The discovery of the virus confirmed this fact and retrospective studies on stored sera confirmed that the virus had not been present in epidemic form in humans, anywhere in the world, before the mid to late 1970s. Since appearing, the virus has now spread to all countries and the numbers of infected individuals and those with AIDS are increasing at an alarming rate. At the time of writing, the total of AIDS cases in the USA alone has exceeded 30 000 of whom approximately 50% have died and the UK, in which the epidemic seems to be running two years behind that in North America, has recorded 600 cases. The estimated numbers of asymptomatic carriers of HIV are currently 1–2 million in the USA and 30 000–50 000 in the UK.

Careful analysis of many thousands of cases of AIDS in many countries has confirmed that the virus is restricted in its transmission to several defined routes. Sexual contact with exchange of body fluids is the main reason for the escalating number of infected individuals and male–to–male, male–to–female and female–to–male transmission has occurred. Any circumstances which allow the transfer of blood or serum from one individual to another confer the risk of infection and transmission has been associated with blood and blood product (particularly Factor VIII) transfusion, sharing of needles and syringes by intravenous drug abusers and (rarely) inoculation injuries to health care staff. In addition to these routes, vertical transmission from an infected mother to her baby is common. This has resulted in an increasingly large number of infected neonates with the risk of progression to AIDS in early life. Apart from the apparent danger that pregnancy in an asymptomatic carrier of HIV may precipitate disease, approximately 50% of the babies of HIV positive mothers appear to be infected (probably *in utero*) and roughly half of those may develop AIDS within two years. Although the virus can be occasionally isolated from several body fluids obtained from infected individuals, e.g. saliva, tears and urine, there is no evidence that these can transmit the infection. Apart from blood and serum, the only other body fluids known to have transmitted infection are semen (during artificial insemination) and possibly breast milk. Indeed, as the receptor for the virus is confined to cells within the blood, brain and other deep seated tissues, it is hardly surprising that this infection can only be spread by exchange of body fluids (and probably living cells). The absence of evidence,from family studies, that the virus can be transmitted by casual and intimate, non-sexual contact emphasizes this point.

The origin of HIV is unknown. Antibody tests performed on stored sera collected, before the onset of the epidemic, in a number of different countries have confirmed that the virus is new to most of the world. Antibody positivity has been claimed in occasional sera collected in central Africa as early as the 1950s. Whether this indicates a low level of infection with HIV or a cross reaction with another retrovirus is not known. It is of interest to note, however, that approximately 50% of vervet monkeys in sub-Saharan Africa are infected with a simian retrovirus that is closely related to HIV.

Clinical effects

After the first seven years of the epidemic, a wide spectrum of clinical effects have been recognized. The proportion of those infected who have developed AIDS varies in different studies between 10 and 30%. The prognosis of full blown AIDS is extremely poor. The overall mortality is roughly 50% but in patients diagnosed at the beginning of the decade it is close to 100%. Nobody has recovered from AIDS either spontaneously, or as a result of any attempted therapy. Less severe manifestations of the infection are commoner and for every AIDS patient there are 5–6 individuals with PGL or other minor illnesses.

Incubation period

The incubation period of AIDS is very variable and it will take many years to know the full implications of infection with HIV. Several studies have shown gradual deterioration in the health of carriers of the virus since the onset of the epidemic and it is likely that an individual, who has managed to remain asymptomatic for many years, may develop AIDS if the immune system is stressed by illness in later life. Alteration of lifestyles may result in lengthening of the incubation period. In the early days of the epidemic, prisoners in New York and New Jersey were found to have mean incubation periods of 14.6 months. Studies in homosexual men suggested incubation periods of 9–22 months, but one patient developed AIDS four years after multiple blood transfusion and there are many individuals who were infected in 1980 who are still in perfect health. Infants infected from their mothers frequently develop symptoms within six months of birth.

Acute illness at seroconversion

Some individuals who have acquired HIV infection develop a mononucleosis-like illness with fever, lymphadenopathy, arthralgia, skin rash and occasionally meningitis. This illness which is of several days duration coincides with the development of antibodies to HIV and is probably caused by circulating immune complexes.

AIDS-related tumours

Kaposi's sarcoma. Kaposi's sarcoma (KS) is a neoplastic vascular disorder which produces multiple violaceous nodules on the skin surface and, as it progresses, may extend to the mucous membranes and internal organs. The tumour appears to originate from the vascular endothelium. Its progression appears to depend on the continuation of an immunocompromised state and there are records of regression of KS in individuals with drug-induced immunosuppression when the therapy has been discontinued.

KS was an extremely rare tumour in most communities before the HIV epidemic. It was occasionally diagnosed in patients receiving long term immunosuppressive therapy and a benign form of the disease was known to occur in elderly men of Jewish or Mediterranean ancestry. In addition there is an endemic form of KS, which can produce disseminated lesions, in Africa; none of these pre-existing forms of KS have been associated with infection with retroviruses. KS has been the sole presenting feature in approximately 30% of AIDS patients during the early years of the epidemic, but it has been almost entirely confined to homosexual men with AIDS. As the virus becomes less confined to this group the incidence of KS is likely to decrease. KS is an opportunistic tumour that develops as a result of the immunosuppression. The factor(s) initiating this malignancy is unknown. Speculation that cytomegalovirus, a very common infection in homosexual men, might be the cause has not been confirmed. It is thought likely that another infectious agent, common in homosexuals, or a lifestyle factor such as the use of certain drugs might be involved.

Other tumours. The HIV epidemic has produced an increase in certain tumours other than KS. B cell and non-Hodgkins lymphomata have now been recognized as opportunistic tumours in AIDS patients. It remains to be seen whether the recent increase in the incidence of anorectal carcinoma in homosexual men is HIV-related.

Opportunistic infections

The immunocompromise induced by the persistence of a replicating retrovirus within the immune system predisposes to infection with a range of opportunistic agents. These may produce disease in many different organs and, as immune function continues to decrease, the patients often suffer from multiple infections. The pattern of infectious agents involved shows some geographical variation which reflects their prevalence in that particular area. Thus *Toxoplasma gondii,* which is common in Haiti, is a common opportunist in AIDS patients in that country.

The commonest opportunistic infection is *Pneumocystis carinii* pneumonia. This protozoal infection has been the presenting feature in about 50% of AIDS patients. Cytomegalovirus is frequently reactivated from its latent state and produces disease in several sites. Cytomegaloviral pneumonia, colitis and encephalitis are all relatively common and choroidoretinitis leads to extensive retinal scarring with progressive blindness. In one study, disseminated cytomegalovirus infection was found to be the major cause of death in AIDS patients. Oral candidiasis is common in AIDS and in patients with milder forms of HIV infection. Extension to the oesophagus occurs as the immune system fails. Perianal herpes simplex infection due to reactivation of latent virus is likely to persist and become progressively more extensive if the patients are not given prophylactic acyclovir.

Opportunistic infections are common in the nervous system and produce several different types of pathology. Cerebral abscesses may be caused by *Toxoplasma gondii* and meningitis due to *Cryptococcus neoformans* has been a common presenting feature of AIDS in African countries. In the later stages of the disease patients have been seen to develop progressive multifocal leucoencephalopathy (see Chapter 12).

Diarrhoea may be a major problem and in some patients there is no obvious opportunist present to account for it. However, a variety of enteric pathogens are described in AIDS including salmonella species and the protozoal disease, cryptosporidiosis.

Mycobacterial infections (*M. tuberculosis* and *M. avium intracellulare*) and *Histoplasma capsulatum* are relatively common pathogens in AIDS patients and their frequency shows geographical variation.

Other presentations of HIV

Persistent generalized lymphadenopathy (PGL). The development of PGL must not be seen as part of a progression of HIV infection from an asymptomatic state to AIDS. Although some individuals with this syndrome proceed to AIDS, the majority remain reasonably well and some lose their lymphadenopathy and return to the asymptomatic carrier state. PGL is defined as palpable lymphadenopathy (node enlargement of 1 cm or greater) at two or more extrainguinal sites persisting for more than three months in the absence of a concurrent illness or condition other than HIV infection to explain the findings. Many patients have no associated symptoms, others experience combinations of fatigue, low grade intermittent fever, night sweats and weight changes, headaches and frequent minor infections. Individuals who have more severe illness attributable to HIV infection but do not have the specific conditions required to justify the diagnosis of AIDS are included in the definition of AIDS-related complex (ARC).

Paediatric AIDS

Infants and children with AIDS have presented with failure to thrive and a high incidence of bacterial and fungal infections. In the later stages the major opportunistic pathogens common in adult AIDS have been prominent. Lymphocytic interstitial pneumonitis developing in children with HIV infection has been attributed to Epstein-Barr virus on the basis of antigen detection in lung tissue.

AIDS dementia complex

This effect, which is thought to result from HIV replication in the brain, is characterized by a triad of cognitive, motor and behavioural dysfunction. It probably affects the majority of AIDS patients; studies in progress will ascertain the frequency of this disturbing manifestation of the infection in otherwise well individuals without immunocompromise.

Laboratory diagnosis

The isolation of the AIDS virus in 1983 was soon followed by the introduction of antibody capture ELISA tests that could be used for screening blood donors. These first generation tests, using crude antigen preparations, produced a significant number of false-positives and a second generation of screening tests including competitive ELISA assays and purified and genetically engineered antigens improved their specificity. Other tests for the presence of antibody are immunofluorescence, western blotting and radioimmune precipitation.

The detection of antibody *per se*, can never indicate more than the fact that an individual has been exposed to the virus at some time. However, from our knowledge of retrovirus infections, and their ability to create a DNA provirus, it must be assumed that the presence of antibody in most individuals indicates persistence of virus. Groups in whom this may not apply are recipients of blood products who may have been immunized with viral antigens and infants, in whom the antibody present in serum may be maternal.

Isolation of virus provides absolute proof of the persistence of HIV infection but the time consuming, expensive and technically difficult nature of this approach renders it unsuitable for diagnostic laboratories at present. The succesful demonstration of HIV antigen in serum, before seroconversion and later in the infectious process, provides a useful index of viral expression and hence the presence of replication.

Prevention and treatment

Worldwide studies are directed towards the development of prototype vaccines and antiviral agents that may be beneficial in the prevention and control of HIV infection. Until these are available the prevention of infection and, hopefully, the control of this global epidemic must be achieved by education of the population to avoid exposure to the virus. This education campaign, aimed at persuading people to avoid casual sexual contact and practise barrier methods of contraception (to prevent exchange of body fluids) has already begun in many countries. Other measures already instituted include screening of donors of blood, semen and organs and the availability of antibody testing for the public at large. Those who are found to be carriers of the virus should receive skilled counselling and psychological support. This includes advice in terms of lifestyle changes and sexual activities and ensures that the infected individuals are fully informed of recent developments.

Patients with AIDS require frequent hospital admission and must be given the benefits of modern diagnostic techniques. This ensures that their tumours and infections can be diagnosed at an early stage so that specific treatment can be applied.

New human retroviruses

One or possibly several newly discovered retroviruses are currently under evaluation. One of these (designated LAV-2 or HIV-2) has been associated with AIDS in West Africa and has also been isolated in Europe. Preliminary antigenic analysis reveals considerable differences between LAV-2 and HIV-1. Sequence analysis of the genome and assessment of its epidemiology and clinical significance are awaited. LAV-2 is known to infect helper T cells and adsorbs to these cells by the CD-4 antigen in a similar manner to HIV-1.

Further reading

Klein E. (Ed) (1986) *Acquired Immunodeficiency Syndrome.* Karger, Basle.

Miller D., Weber J. and Green J. (Eds) (1986) *The Management of AIDS patients.* Macmillan, Basingstoke.

Pinching A. J. (1986) *AIDS and HIV infection.* Clinics in Allergy and Immunology. W. B. Saunders, London.

Chapter 17
Haemorrhagic Fever

The syndrome of haemorrhagic fever is found in many parts of the world and is caused by a number of different viral agents. The clinical presentations of these infections are similar. Following a prodromal febrile illness, patients show signs of haemorrhage into the skin (petechiae and purpura) and from mucous membranes and the severity of these systemic infections may produce bone marrow depression, shock, hypotension, encephalopathy and death. Not every person infected with the haemorrhagic fever viruses develops this syndrome. Asymptomatic infections are common and many individuals suffer the early febrile illness but do not develop the haemorrhagic manifestations.

Arbovirus infections

Arbovirus infections, previously described in the context of epidemic encephalitis (Chapter 12) are important causes of haemorrhagic fever and their distribution, as with other arboviral diseases, shows considerable geographic variation.

Togaviridae of the Flavivirus genus are reponsible for dengue, Kyasanur Forest disease, Omsk haemorrhagic fever and yellow fever.

1. Dengue

Dengue is transmitted by mosquitoes of which *Aedes aegypti* is the most important vector. It is endemic in India, the Far East, Hawaii and the Caribbean, and outbreaks have occurred in recent years in the south-eastern USA and Australia. Two types of disease process are produced by this virus; the common, uncomplicated, non-fatal form that is found in all areas, and dengue haemorrhagic fever, the much more severe and potentially fatal disease that is now mainly confined to Asia. The uncomplicated form has an incubation period of 5–8 days and begins abruptly with a severe headache, retro-orbital pain and generalized severe aching with profound myalgia. The high fever (usually 40°C) persists for 3–6 days, then subsides, but often rises again after an afebrile period of about two days. This biphasic fever has been given the name of a 'saddle-back' response. A morbilliform or scarlatiniform rash often develops on the trunk, at 3–5 days after onset, and spreads to the face and extremities. Desquamation may occur as the rash fades. Generalized lymphadenopathy is present and leucopenia is prominent. The illness usually induces a prolonged period of debility after the acute phase. Dengue haemorrhagic fever occurs in individuals who have pre-existing antibody to the virus. The early symptoms resemble the uncomplicated disease but the patient's condition rapidly worsens and is associated with hypoproteinaemia, thrombocytopenia, prolonged bleeding time and elevated prothrombin time. The more severely affected bleed from the gastro-intestinal tract and from the skin and mucous membranes and a shock syndrome, with haemoconcentration, hypotension and agitation, may supervene. The mortality rate in haemorrhagic dengue is 5–10%. The pathogenesis of the haemorrhagic disease is thought to be due to the existence of four serotypes of the virus which have cross-reacting antigens but fail to confer lasting protection to heterologous types. Thus, infection with a second serotype stimulates a secondary immune response against the original strain and this IgG binds to, but does not neutralize, the new infecting virus. There is evidence that combination of dengue virus with non-neutralizing antibody enhances its infectivity and also produces damage from circulating immune complexes, including disseminated intravascular coagulation. There is no specific antiviral therapy available for dengue, nor indeed for any of the viral haemorrhagic fevers. Management rests in supportive care including intravenous therapy when appropriate and blood transfusion if haemorrhage is severe. The diagnosis and general approaches to prevention of arbovirus infections were described in Chapter 12.

Kyasanur Forest disease

Kyasanur Forest disease was first discovered in Mysore, India in 1957 following an outbreak with deaths in humans and wild monkeys. The reservoir of the virus consists of small rodents (voles and forest rats) and it is transmitted by several species of hard ticks (genus Haemaphysalis). It presents, after an incubation period of 4–8 days, with an illness resembling dengue. A similar biphasic fever occurs, with an intervening afebrile period of 10–20 days. The second fever may be complicated with meningoencephalitis and mental changes. Haemorrhage occurs 3–4 days after the onset of illness and death results from blood loss and shock in the second week. Severe leucopenia and thrombocytopenia are present at the acute stage. The mortality in the initial outbreak was about 5%. In addition to the serological diagnostic tests applicable to arboviral infections this disease is characterized by a prolonged period of viraemia and isolation from serum can be achieved in suckling mice and in tissue cultures.

Omsk haemorrhagic fever

This disease is very similar to Kyasanur Forest disease and occurs in western Siberia. The reservoir persists in water voles and ground squirrels and it is transmitted by Dermacentor ticks. The mortality is approximately 3%.

Yellow fever

After an incubation period of 3–6 days, yellow fever presents with an acute onset of fever, chills, headache and backache followed by nausea and vomiting. This prodrome remits briefly and then the fever increases, in association with a slow pulse rate, and jaundice develops. In severe cases, marked proteinuria and haemorrhages appear and the vomitus may be black due to the presence of large volumes of altered blood. The disease has a high mortality in patients who suffer severe haemorrhage (40–50%). No sequelae develop in those who recover.

Monkey inoculation studies indicate the pathogenesis of yellow fever. Following percutaneous infection, the virus enters the local lymph nodes where it replicates. It then enters the circulation and is conveyed to the liver, spleen, lymph nodes, bone marrow and kidneys where further replication takes place. Necrosis of liver and kidney tissue account for the major effects of the illness, and centrilobular necrosis with inflammatory infiltration causes the jaundice. Degenerative changes are present in the other tissues involved in viral replication and infection may involve the brain.

Two cycles of transmission of yellow fever virus are recognized from epidemiological studies; urban and sylvatic (or jungle). Urban yellow fever is transmitted by Aedes mosquitoes that breed in water accumulations close to dwellings. The virus is transmitted from one human to another by mosquito bites and a constant influx of susceptible individuals ensures the maintenance of the cycle. This form exists in Africa, but has been virtually eliminated from South America by eradication of mosquito breeding areas. Sylvatic yellow fever is primarily a disease of monkeys that is transmitted between monkeys by arboreal mosquitoes (Haemagogus and Aedes) inhabiting the forest canopy. Humans risk infection when they visit areas (forests of South America and Africa) where infected mosquitoes are prevalent. The virus establishes persistent infections within the mosquitoes and a period of 12–14 days elapses after ingestion of infected blood before the establishment of a productive infection in the salivary glands (the extrinsic incubation period).

Virus can be isolated from the blood of infected humans during the first five days of illness by intracerebral inoculation of mice.

An excellent attenuated, live vaccine (17D strain) produces immunity to yellow fever that persists for over ten years. This is prepared in eggs and, apart from the problems associated with egg hypersensitivity, it is remarkably free from side effects.

3. Crimean-Congo haemorrhagic fever

Crimean-Congo haemorrhagic fever virus is a Bunyavirus which is transmitted by infected ticks. The natural reservoir is in wild and domesticated animals including sheep, goats, cattle and hares and the virus is found in the Crimea and central Asia, equatorial Africa and Pakistan. The disease is similar in length of incubation period (4–8 days), prodromal illness and appearance of haemorrhages to other haemorrhagic fevers, but meningoencephalitis dominates the later course of the disease and this contributes to the high mortality rate (approximately 50%).

Arenaviruses

Lassa fever

Lassa fever is named after a village in north east Nigeria where the first outbreak was recognized in 1969. It is caused by a member of the Arenaviridae and related viruses are also associated with haemorrhagic fever (see below).

The reservoir of the virus is the multimammate rat, *Mastomys natalensis*, and the disease is endemic in Nigeria, Liberia and Sierra Leone. The distribution of Mastomys is much wider, in Africa, than Lassa fever virus. Man is infected from the urine of the persistently infected rats. The rats enter dwellings in rural communities in search of food and, when crawling along beams and rafters, urinate on the sleeping inhabitants and their fomites below. The portal of entry of the virus is unknown but it is assumed that infection occurs from ingestion or inhalation. The presence of virus in the throat at the acute stage of the illness suggests that it may be transmitted by airborne dissemination between humans; inoculation injury has resulted in transmission. Many asymptomatic infections occur as evidenced by serological surveys in endemic areas. Haemorrhage appears to result from a combination of capillary damage, thrombocytopenia and coagulation abnormalities. The incubation period is 7–17 days and the prodromal symptoms usually start gradually with a fever, malaise, chills and severe muscle pains. Sore throat with a white or yellowish exudate becomes a prominent feature and this may be so severe that swallowing is inhibited. Many patients complain of headache and abdominal pain. This non-specific illness may persist for a week before haemorrhages appear, but severe infections often pursue a more accelerated course. Signs of capillary leakage, facial oedema, pleural effusion and ecchymoses occur with clinical deterioration and herald the onset of multiple haemorrhages. Shock does not feature until the terminal stages.

The diagnosis should be suspected in anyone, presenting with an unexplained fever, who has returned within 21 days from an endemic area. Lassa fever can usually be eliminated if the individual has been resident in a city or if another diagnosis is reached (e.g. malaria). If there is an element of doubt, migrants to the United Kingdom are transferred to high security infectious disease units where, if necessary, they are nursed in plastic isolators. Virus present in throat swabs, blood and urine can be isolated in cell cultures and serological diagnosis is achieved by complement fixation, indirect immunofluorescence and neutralization tests.

Convalescent plasma has been given to patients with acute infection to reduce viraemia and trials of the antiviral drug, ribavirin, conducted in Sierra Leone have shown some promise. The mortality of Lassa fever in those admitted to hospital has been 40–50%, but the occurrence of asymptomatic and mild infections probably indicates a much lower overall figure.

Argentine and Bolivian haemorrhagic fever

Argentine and Bolivian hemorrhagic fever are caused by two arenaviruses, Junin virus and Machupo virus respectively, that produce illnesses similar to Lassa fever in South America. The viruses are transmitted to humans from the urine of the primary hosts, rodents of the genus Calomys.

Korean haemorrhagic fever (Haemorrhagic fever with renal syndrome)

As its name suggests Korean haemorrhagic fever virus, presumed to be a member of the Bunyaviridae, is endemic to Korea and surrounding areas of the Far East. Recently, similar agents have been associated with haemorrhagic renal syndromes throughout northern Europe and Asia and virus has been isolated from wild rodents in the USA. Rats and voles appear to be the main reservoirs and, in the absence of an obvious vector, exposure to rodent urine is thought to be the main route of infection.

The incubation period of 10–30 days is followed by a high fever, malaise, myalgia, headache and photophobia. Erythema of the face and neck produces a sunburnt appearance. After 3–6 days the temperature falls but this is no cause for optimism as it is accompanied by hypotension and heralds the onset of more severe illness. Haemorrhages develop together with abdominal pain, vomiting and renal failure with oliguria or anuria predominate the clinical picture. The most severely affected become delirious and shocked and death in coma, preceded by convulsions, follows. In those who recover, the symptoms usually subside suddenly and the oliguric phase is followed by a prolonged diuretic phase accompanied by marked thirst. The mortality depends on the quality of care and probably on the strain of virus involved. In some early outbreaks the mortality was 15–30% but careful management of American troops infected in Korea reduced this to 6%.

Specific diagnosis is achieved by indirect immunofluorescence using infected tissue as the source of antigen.

Marburg virus disease

Marburg virus disease is a haemorrhagic fever with a high mortality, named after the city in which the most cases occurred when it first appeared in 1967. Marburg virus contains RNA and produces filamentous particles 100 nm diameter and 300–1500 nm long. With Ebola virus (see below) it has been classified as a member of the new family, Filoviridae. The outbreak in 1967 originated in a group of vervet (green) monkeys shipped from Uganda to vaccine manufacturers in Marburg in Germany, and Yugoslavia. For this reason, the disease was known as green monkey disease. Since then two further small outbreaks have occurred in South Africa (1974) and Kenya (1980). Of 36 cases recorded to date, 27 have been primary infections and nine secondary, via human contacts. The incubation periods for primary attacks were 3–7 days and in secondary cases, 5–9 days. The virus is thought to lose virulence on passage in the human as the most severe cases and all the fatalities were in primary cases. Viraemia and fever lasting for about 14 days is accompanied by necrosis in various organs. The virus showed evidence of persistence for several months in liver, semen and ocular fluid and sexual transmission from a convalescent male is recorded. Fatalities occurred at the acute stage and were associated with haemorrhage, severe patchy liver necrosis and encephalitis. All patients developed a maculopapular rash after 5–8 days of the illness and in the most severe cases this changed to a dark red erythema. On resolution desquamation was observed. Half the patients haemorrhaged from day four into the skin, mucous membranes, gastrointestinal and urinary tracts. Despite evidence of a severe hepatitis, jaundice was very rare. Myocarditis with arrhythmias and cardiac failure was common during the crisis period and deaths were attributed to cardiac failure, renal failure and encephalitis. Profound leucopenia and thrombocytopenia, possibly suggesting disseminated intravascular coagulation were consistently present. Twenty five per cent of patients have died. All three outbreaks have had an African connection and although the reservoir of Marburg virus is unknown it is likely to exist in that continent. Strict isolation must be applied to suspected sufferers. The virus may be cultured in Vero cells (a continuous vervet monkey line).

Ebola virus disease

Ebola is clinically very similar to Marburg virus disease and the virus, although antigenically unrelated, is very similar morphologically. As with Marburg virus, the natural host of Ebola virus is unknown. The first known epidemic of Ebola was in 1976 on the Sudan–Zaire border and 600 cases were identified. A further outbreak arose in the same district in 1979. Detailed studies of the pathogenesis are not available. The incubation period averages seven days (range 4–16) and, as with Marburg disease there is a marked viraemia with multisystem involvement. There is also some evidence of viral persistence in semen. Part of our knowledge of the clinical picture comes from a relatively mild case that occurred in a laboratory worker in England. A sudden onset of fever, gastrointestinal symptoms and limb pains is followed by diarrhoea, pharyngitis and a dry cough. By day five, anicteric hepatitis, morbilliform exanthema and haemorrhagic effects have appeared in severe cases. Encephalopathy may be a further complication. Two antigenic subtypes were recognized; the Zairian strains had a mortality of 90% and those from Sudan, 55%.

Further reading

Bowen E. T. W., Lloyd G., Harris W. J. *et al.* (1977) Viral haemorrhagic fever in southern Sudan and northern Zaire. *Lancet*, **i**, 571–3.

Braude A. I. (1986) *Infectious Diseases and Medical Microbiology*. W. B. Saunders, Philadelphia.

Johnson K. M. (1979) Arthropod-borne viral fevers. In: *Cecil Textbook of Medicine*, 15th edition. Beeson P. B. *et al.* (Eds). W. B. Saunders, Philadelphia.

Monath T. P. (1975) Lassa fever: review of epidemiology and epizootiology. *WHO Bulletin*, **52**, 577.

Pang T. (1983) Delayed-type hypersensitivity: probable role in the pathogenesis of dengue haemorrhagic fever/dengue shock syndrome. *Rev Inf Dis*, **5**, 346–52.

Chapter 18
Poxviruses

Few achievements in the 20th century can compare with the global eradication of smallpox. The last case of this dangerous virus infection occurred in 1977 and, in 1979, the world was declared smallpox-free. In a world so fraught by conflict it is pleasing to reflect on this triumph that resulted from scientific and medical knowledge and research, logic, masterly organization and international collaboration. The disappearance of smallpox relegates the Poxviridae to a very minor role in the overall consideration of human viral diseases. Smallpox eradication has also eliminated another much less damaging virus, yet one that has caused serious iatrogenic disease and death, the vaccine virus, vaccinia. Many books provide excellent and detailed accounts of smallpox. This short chapter is presented to summarize

Table 18.1 Animal poxviruses

Viruses	Human infection
Orthopoxviruses	
Cowpox, monkeypox (variola, vaccinia)	+
Mousepox, camelpox, buffalopox	—
Parapoxviruses	
Orf, milkers nodes	+
Avipoxviruses	
Fowlpox, canarypox	—
Leporipoxviruses	
Myxoma, fibroma	—
Capripoxviruses	
Goat pox, sheep pox	—
Unclassfied	
Yaba, tanapox	+
Swinepox	—

the nature of the disease and to present short accounts of other poxvirus infections. The family, Poxviridae, is subdivided as shown in Table 18.1. Members of the orthopoxvirus subgroup cross-react immunologically and confer protective immunity to each other.

Smallpox (variola)

The mortality of smallpox varied considerably from less than 1% to 40% and although different strains were associated with particular geographical regions the pathogenicity was due to the virus and not local host susceptibility. This was evident when migrants carried the viruses with them to new areas; the pattern of disease and its mortality were similar to that found in the source country.

Pathogenesis

The portal of entry of variola virus was the mucous membranes of the upper respiratory tract. Knowledge of the nature of the disease processes and study of systemic poxvirus diseases of animals led to the hypothesis that the pathogenesis of smallpox was based on the development of primary and secondary viraemias, the sequence probably occurring as follows. After initial replication in lymph nodes draining the implantation site, the virus was disseminated (primary viraemia) to the reticuloendothelial system. Extensive replication in multiple areas resulted in the secondary viraemia that heralded the onset of the disease. This intense viraemia deposited virus in skin capillaries with resultant invasion of the prickle cell layer. These cells proliferated and contained cytoplasmic inclusions indicating active viral replication. Extensive inflammation was associated with mononuclear cell infiltration and disruption of the membranes of vacuolated epithelial cells led to the formation of vesicles. The vesicles were thicker walled than those characteristically found in herpes virus infections and extension into dermal tissues meant that, if the patient recovered, permanent scarring of the skin remained. The oedema caused by this highly cytocidal virus caused considerable thickening of the skin and the patient often lost facial features to become virtually unrecognizable at the acute stage. The most severe forms produced widespread haemorrhages in the skin without the normal sequences of vesication, ulceration and subsequent healing by crusting. Death usually occurred swiftly in haemorrhagic smallpox.

Epidemiology

The transmission rate of smallpox from an infected individual to susceptible contacts was approximately 35%. Although most cases could be traced to contact with infected cases, there were well documented outbreaks resulting from exposure to virus on fomites. Persistence of virus in dust and crust material was responsible for an outbreak in laundry workers. Successful vaccination produced solid immunity for 3–5 years and modified the illness resulting from exposure after that time. Full protection was rapidly restored by revaccination. The first strategies for eradication were based on mass vaccination in attempts to exclude the virus from a population by generating high levels of herd immunity. This failed and smallpox epidemics were seen to occur in areas where over 90% of the population had been vaccinated. This knowledge led to the adoption of the policy of identification and isolation of cases and vaccination of contacts. It was this approach that proved so successful in the WHO eradication campaign. The rationale for proceeding with eradiction rested on two important premises. First that there was no animal reservoir for smallpox and second that there was no state of persistence of the virus in humans. These assumptions seemed correct, as countries which had been rendered smallpox-free had remained free from new cases for several years. Difficulties in obtaining reports of possible cases were overcome by introducing financial rewards for those who could locate the disease. Endemic areas were constantly and repeatedly surveyed to ensure that no cases were missed.

Clinical effects

The incubation period was normally about 12 days. A prodromal illness with fever, malaise, myalgia and headache usually preceded the rash by 1–5 days. The rash appeared first as red papules and then over 1–3 days developed into the typical deep-set, thick-walled vesicles that often became umbilicated. The lesions gradually turned from vesicles containing clear fluid to pustules and these formed crusts that were shed within four weeks of onset of the rash. Smallpox had two features which were of use in its differential diagnosis from varicella.

1 Lesions in one part of the body were all at the same stage of maturation, unlike the varicella rash in which the repeated viraemias produce all stages of lesions from papules to ulcers.

2 The rash in smallpox was centrifugal with lesions being particularly intense on the prominences; the varicella rash is centripetal, i.e. denser on the trunk and in the axillae and groins.

The patient's fever usually subsided 24–48 hours after the onset of the rash but a secondary rise was frequently observed at the pustular stage possibly due to the absorption of toxic products of the extensive cellular necrosis in the skin or to secondary bacterial infection of the skin lesions (or both). The clinical condition of the patient could be correlated with the extent and nature of the rash and those who had a very minor rash due to previous vaccination often experienced mild symptoms or were asymptomatic. Those with mild smallpox were particularly dangerous as they could travel, work, and, by mixing with others, transmit the infection to more vulnerable hosts. Patients were most infectious when the skin lesions started to rupture and release large amounts of virus. The rupture of similar lesions in the mouth was probably an important source for the transmission of the disease to others. Variola was a resistant virus that could persist for prolonged periods at room temperature. Thus, patients were isolated and assumed to be potentially infectious until after the last crust had disappeared and healing had taken place. This is a further feature that was distinctive from varicella in which the virus in vesicles soon becomes undetectable and, due to its relative fragility, does not persist in crust material.

Laboratory diagnosis

Smallpox presented a serious risk to public health and the increase in quantity and speed of travel over the last few decades increased the danger to countries that had eliminated endemic disease. Rapid diagnosis with isolation of suspects and vaccination of contacts was of utmost importance and, atypical forms of the disease occurring particularly in those who had been previously vaccinated, often rendered clinical diagnosis unreliable. Laboratory diagnosis reached a high level of development and several techniques were usually used concurrently. Electron microscopy frequently provided a rapid answer to the question 'is it a poxvirus or a herpesvirus infection?'. The rectangular particles of poxviruses (300 × 200 nm) are easily distinguished from the particles of herpes viruses (100 nm icosahedra with surrounding membranes). This technique did not allow an accurate diagnosis due to the morphological similarities of individual members of each family, but it often directed the future management of the patient. If no particles were observed, the technique was non-contributory. Fluid from vesicles, or extracts of crusts, were examined for the presence of antigen using immunodiffusion methods. A result could often be obtained in several hours. The most sensitive test for the presence of virus was culture on the chorioallantoic membrane of 12–14 day fertile hens' eggs. Pocks present on the membrane after three days incubation indicated the growth of a pox virus or herpes simplex viruses (varicella-zoster does not grow in the egg) and the size, morphology and appearance of the pocks allowed them to be distinguished.

Vaccinia virus

Vaccinia virus was used for many years to immunize against smallpox infection. Before the introduction of the technique of vaccination with material from cowpox lesions by Edward Jenner in 1798, attempts had been made to induce immunity by variolation; this was the inoculation of material from active smallpox lesions into susceptible individuals. The origins of vaccinia virus are lost in obscurity; restriction enzyme and base sequence analysis of vaccinia and cowpox strains may eventually explain their relationships. Large stocks of vaccinia were prepared in the skin of calves or in chick embryos and stored frozen or lyophilized. The vaccinia was deposited in the skin of the deltoid region or thigh by several techniques (multiple puncture, scratching or jet injection). Successful replication of the virus in the skin with resulting immunity produced a localized lesion that went through the typical poxvirus progression of papule, vesicle, pustule and crust formation. This reaction proceeded more rapidly following revaccination due to the recall of pre-existing immunity.

This relatively harmless live vaccine saved numerous lives but it was not without occasional complications. In the United Kingdom, those who strongly advocated the abandonment of routine vaccination in the early 1970s pointed out that in that non-endemic area, vaccination had killed over four times as many people in the previous 20 years than had smallpox itself.

The four important complications of vaccination were:

Eczema vaccinatum

Vaccinia virus had a tendency to become disseminated in eczematous skin. This effect could have serious consequences in those with severe atopic states and the resulting generalized rash was often fatal. A similar state of compromise is seen in atopic individuals infected with herpes simplex viruses (eczema herpeticum, see Chapter 9).

Post-vaccinial encephalitis

This serious complication of vaccination accounted for many of the deaths that led to the abandonment of its use as a routine. The disease was described in Chapter 12. It was almost totally associated with primary vaccination and its incidence was higher in the first year of life (and in adults) than in older children.

Progressive vaccinia (vaccinia gangrenosa)

This rare reaction occurred when vaccine was administered to people who had immune deficiency states. The vaccination site continued to enlarge and produce a large necrotic ulcer with the persistence of infectious virus. This resulted in death in some individuals.

Neonatal vaccinia

Vaccination in the later stages of pregnancy could infect the baby *in utero* with the development of large, atypical vesicles which were present on the skin at the time of birth.

Cowpox

Cowpox is occasionally evident in cows as a vesicular eruption on the teats and udders. Human infections can be acquired by implantation of the virus into skin lesions and traditionally this disease is associated with milk-maids. As with several other viruses this virus has been misnamed as many cases of human cowpox have arisen in people who have not been in contact with cows and inspection and serological testing of herds has not revealed persistence in that species. The cow is probably an occasional sufferer in a similar way to the human and the primary host is likely to be a rodent.

In the human the main lesion is a vesicle at the site of implantation and this is often accompanied by regional lymphadenitis. Systemic effects, particularly fever and malaise are sometimes present at the acute stage. The disease normally resolves in 2–3 weeks without sequelae.

Monkeypox

This orthopoxvirus was so named because it was first recognized as a severe infection in captive monkeys. No simian outbreaks in nature have been recorded, and the severe disease produced in monkeys suggests that this virus is normally present in a different host. After the eradication of smallpox from West African countries in the 1960s, several sporadic cases of a severe poxvirus infection that were clinically identical to smallpox were reported from several countries. Laboratory analysis of isolation material revealed that the aetiological agent was monkeypox, an orthopoxvirus, quite distinct from variola. Most of these cases were in children and the disease severity, mortality, long term scarring and other sequelae were similar to the type of smallpox that had pre-existed in those countries. Since the first known case, in 1970, reports of occasional sporadic cases have continued. These cases would not have been distinguished from smallpox when the disease was endemic in those areas. The extensive smallpox vaccination campaigns that resulted in elimination of the disease from West Africa may have suppressed a low background incidence of monkeypox; vaccination confers protection to both orthopoxviruses. Waning of immunity and the increasing numbers of susceptible children may have increased the incidence of this zoonotic poxvirus disease. Fears that monkeypox might become epidemic and fill the ecological niche vacated by smallpox have been largely dispelled with the knowledge that monkeypox virus does not transmit readily to susceptibles. The virus infects approximately 5% of susceptible close contacts as compared with a transmission rate for variola of 35%.

Orf

Orf is classified as a parapoxvirus. It is immunologically distant from the orthopoxviruses and vaccination offers no protection against this disease. The virus is also morphologically distinct and, on negative staining, it can be recognized by the characteristic spiral arrangement of its surface subunits. Orf is primarily a disease of sheep that occurs particularly in lambs during spring and summer and causes a papulovesicular eruption around the mouth. Infection in man usually takes the form of a solitary lesion on the hand or forearm and most patients have had direct contact with sheep. A papule soon develops into a flat vesicle (often 1 cm diameter) and this resolves without scarring in 2–3 weeks. There is not usually significant systemic disturbance.

Molluscum contagiosum

This common virus infection produces benign tumours (2–5 mm diameter) on the skin surface anywhere on the body except the palms and the soles. The lesions are pearly white in colour and painless and close inspection reveals a central aperture through which can be seen a white core. They are often seen to cluster in affected parts of the body. Resolution is spontaneous and usually occurs within several months. Expression of the core material reveals hypertrophied cells containing cytoplasmic masses called molluscum bodies. On electron microscopy these are seen to be full of viral particles. Infection occurs by skin–to–skin contact, the virus probably gaining access to the epidermis through minor abrasions.

Further reading

Behbehani A. M. (1983) The smallpox story: life and death of an old disease. *Microbiol Rev*, **47**, 455.

Breman J. G. and Arita I. (1980) The confirmation and maintenance of smallpox eradication. *New Engl J Med*, **303**, 1236.

Dixon C. W. (1962) *Smallpox*. Churchill Livingstone, London.

Chapter 19
Viruses and Cancer

Viruses have been known to cause cancer in animals since the early years of the 20th century. Ellerman and Bang and Peyton Rous reported the transmission of avian tumours by cell-free extracts of tumour cells between 1908 and 1911. These viruses were later recognized as retroviruses. Others, Shope (1933) and Gross (1953), pioneered work with papovaviruses with their identification of agents that caused benign papillomata in rabbits and parotid tumours in laboratory mice. Further work led to the discovery that viruses from several other families have oncogenic potential by possessing the ability to alter the growth characteristics (transform) cultured cells and to induce malignancy in laboratory animals, often of a different species from the natural host of the virus. There is now no doubt that viruses have a major aetiological role in the induction of benign and malignant tumours in animals. The ability of human papillomaviruses to induce benign tumours (warts) has been known for many years and some varieties of warts have been associated with the tendency to undergo malignant change. Recent investigations have firmly implicated several different viruses in having important roles in the initiation of human cancers. Epstein–Barr virus infection is central to the development of Burkitt's lymphoma and nasopharyngeal carcinoma and particular subtypes of papillomaviruses are considered to be the primary cause of cervical carcinoma. The discovery of human T cell leukaemia virus type 1 (HTLV-1) led to its acceptance as the major aetiological agent of a geographically clustered adult T cell leukaemia and the prevalence of hepatoma in areas of high hepatitis B incidence, together with other evidence, implicates persistent infection with this virus in tumourigenesis. Identification of cellular genomic sequences (cellular oncogenes), ubiquitous in DNA, that are mirrored in animal retroviruses with potent oncogenic potential has led to their recognition as controlling elements in tumour development. Oncogenes have been considered as the final common pathway in malignant change and their activation, by any (or probably several) of the known genetic or environmental factors associated with tumour initiation, is thought likely to lead to the clonal expansion of a cancer cell.

Thus, to consider the possible role of viruses in human cancer is, perhaps, to take a brief glimpse into the future. The increasingly large research commitment in these, and other, areas of virology is likely to produce further clarification of oncogenesis. Hopefully, developments in molecular biology and chemotherapy will provide ways of combating the viral components in malignant change.

Mechanisms of oncogenesis

In assessing the possible factors involved in the development of tumours it must be remembered that all carcinogenesis is likely to be multifactorial in origin. Epidemiological evidence indicates that a variety of influences (genetic and environmental) are likely to be necessary for cancer to develop and infection with a virus or activation of a cellular oncogene may be one of these.

Genetic factors

Exposure to ionizing radiation and chemical carcinogens results in alterations in gene arrangements in DNA and the extent of this disturbance has been correlated with mutagenicity in animal cells and carcinogenicity *in vivo*. Family traits indicate a genetic predisposition to cancer development and particular inherited syndromes are commonly associated with cancer. An example of this is the rare autosomal recessive disease, epidermodysplasia verruciformis, which is characterized by extensive infection with a range of different papillomavirus types. One third of these patients develop squamous cell carcinoma, usually in areas exposed to sunlight. The induction of malignancy by genetic disturbance presupposes the clonal expansion of a single altered cell and the oligoclonal nature of malignant tumours supports this hypothesis. The initiation of a clone of potentially malignant cells may not necessarily lead to tumour formation. Spontaneous regression of established human cancers (e.g. neuroblastoma) has been noted and widespread Kaposi's sarcoma occurring in individuals receiving immunosuppressive drugs has been seen to resolve if the therapy has been discontinued. This probably indicates the important role of immune surveillance in countering the development of potentially malignant cells which, some believe, are being continually generated.

Specific genes in oncogenesis

Studies of the genomic structure of animal retroviruses have led to the identification of sequences in host DNA (cellular oncogenes) that are homologous with retroviral genes (viral oncogenes) capable of inducing malignancy in animals. Activation of cellular oncogenes has been associated with malignant transformation of cells. They have been found to be present at the sites of integration of viruses and chromosomal translocations incriminated in tumour formation. They have also been detected in the DNA derived from naturally occurring or chemically induced tumour cells. Continuing analysis of these genes and investigations of the function of their products should assist our understanding of malignancy. Their role in normal cell function is ill-defined, but there is evidence that they are active and important during prenatal development. The viral oncogenes are thought to have been derived from cellular DNA and those that have been identified are listed, with some detail of their products, in Table 19.1. The acquisition of an oncogene by a retrovirus appears to confer enhanced neoplastic qualities to the newly integrated RNA copy of the cellular sequence. Indeed, the infection of cells with oncogene-containing retroviruses is associated with the initiation of acute malignancies. This type of retrovirus is illustrated in Fig. 19.1a. Most retroviruses do not possess integrated viral oncogenes and many appear to trigger tumour formation by insertion into the host cell genome adjacent to, and thereby activating, a cellular oncogene (Fig. 19.1b). The retrovirus HTLV-1 does not contain a viral oncogene and integrates randomly in the T lymphocyte genome. If malignant transformation occurs it appears to be unrelated to the proximity of the integrated HTLV-1 provirus with cellular oncogenes. As illustrated in Fig. 19.1c, the genome incorporates a highly conserved region, X, that encodes a protein thought to activate cellular genes leading to neoplastic transformation. Most of the DNA viruses associated with the capacity to induce malignant change have the ability to insert a portion of the viral genome into the host cell chromosome. Some DNA viruses have also been incriminated as possible cofactors in promoting tumour development by disturbing cellular replication (the so-called hit and run hypothesis) but there is no firm evidence for this. With DNA tumour viruses, the viral genome contains early and late regions. The late region consists of genes that code for the synthesis of viral coat proteins which are not expressed in transformed cells. The early region of the genome is expressed soon after infection

Table 19.1 Retroviral oncogenes

Oncogene	Product
src fes, fps fgr	Tyrosine phosphokinases or structurally related proteins
erb-B	Epidermal growth factor
sis	Platelet derived growth factor
ras	GTP-ase
myc	DNA-binding
yes abl ros mos mil, raf myb fms erb-A fos ets ski rel	Product unknown

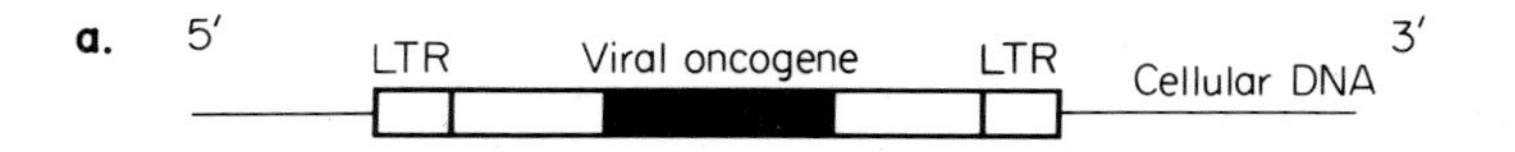

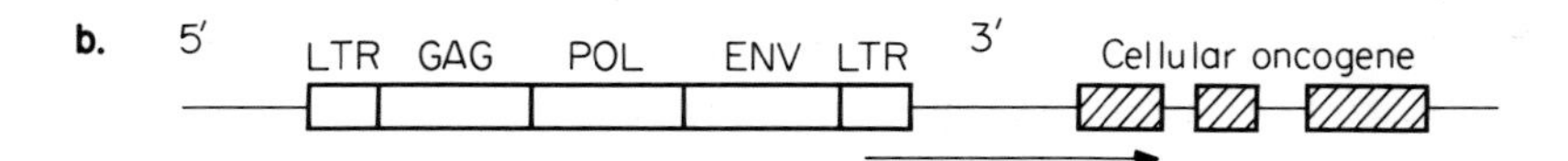

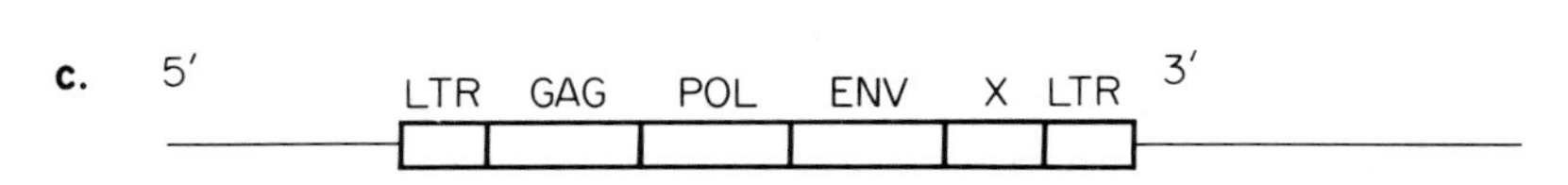

Fig. 19.1 Diagrams to illustrate the structures of different types of oncogenic retroviruses. LTR = long terminal repeat sequences. GAG, POL and ENV genes code respectively for the internal proteins, reverse transcriptases and envelope glycoproteins of the viruses.

Table 19.2 Human viruses with oncogenic properties

Family	Viruses	Associated tumour	Possible cofactors.
Adenovirus	Types 2, 5, 12	None	
Hepadnavirus	Hepatitis B	Hepatocellular carcinoma	Aflatoxin, alcohol
Herpes	Epstein–Barr virus	Burkitt's lymphoma Immunoblastic lymphoma Nasopharyngeal carcinoma	Malaria Immunocompromise Nitrosamines
	Herpes simplex type II	Cervical neoplasia (?)	
Papovavirus	Papillomavirus	Warts	
		Cervical neoplasia	Smoking, Herpes simplex(?)
		Skin cancer	Genetic disorders, (epidermodysplasia verruciformis), sunlight
	Polyomavirus (BK, JC)	Neural tumours (?)	
Retroviruses	HTLV-1	Adult T cell leukaemia—lymphoma.	

of the cells and contains genes which code for early proteins necessary for viral DNA replication and for the transformation of non-permissive cells. The transforming protein must be continually synthesized for the cells to stay transformed. The viruses currently associated with human malignancy are listed in Table 19.2.

Human papillomaviruses

Papillomaviruses infect man and a wide range of animals. Their association with benign tumours, human warts and animal papillomata, has been recognized for years but research has been handicapped by the lack of suitable culture systems. Recent association of specific types of papillomavirus with cervical neoplasia has stimulated intensive investigation into their pathogenicity. Many different types of human papillomavirus (HPV) have now been identified on the basis of genomic differences and their disease associations are listed in Table 19.3. The lack of culture systems continues and viruses are compared by harvesting the DNA from papilloma lesions and comparing its nucleotide homology with known virus DNA. If a virus has 50% or greater DNA homology with a known virus it is classified as that type. If the homology is <50% it is designated a new type of Papillomavirus. Four HPV types are associated with neoplastic changes in the genital tract; HPV 6, 11, 16 and 18.

Papillomaviruses infect the basal layers of squamous epithelium and, although viral DNA is present in these cells, no viral structural proteins are present. Full replication occurs only in differentiated squamous epithelium and infectious virions are present in the most superficial cells. Viral DNA enters the nuclei of cells in the basal layer where it replicates independently of the chromosomes as an episome. The presence of the viral genome stimulates the proliferation of the epithelial cells with the resultant development of warts or papillomata. Production of mature virions at the surface leads to the release of infectious virus that allows transmission to a new host.

The malignant conversion of papillomata in animals has been noted since Rous and Beard (1935) described malignant change in 25% of benign warts in the cottontail rabbit. In 1981, Jarrett and colleagues described the development of squamous carcinomata in cattle from oesophageal, intestinal and bladder papillomata (produced by bovine papillomavirus type 4), when the animals were fed on bracken which is known to contain a potent carcinogen. The virus was detectable in the benign lesions but not in the carcinomata. The significance of epidermodysplasia verruciformis was discussed earlier.

Table 19.3 Diseases associated with human papillomaviruses (HPV)

HPV types	Clinical condition
1a–c	Plantar warts
2a–e	Hand warts
3a, b	Flat warts, juvenile warts
4	Plantar warts
5a, b	Macules in EV
6a	Condylomata acuminata, CIN 1–3, VIN 1–3, laryngeal papilloma
7	Butchers' warts
8	Macules in EV
9	Warts and macules in EV
10a, b	Flat warts
11a, b	Condylomata acuminata, CIN 1–3, laryngeal papilloma
12	Warts and macules in EV
13	Hyperplastic neck lesions
14a, b	EV
15	EV
16	Condylomata acuminata, CIN 1–3, VIN 1–3, carcinoma of cervix and penis
17a, b	EV
18	Carcinoma of cervix and penis
19–29	Warts in EV
30	Laryngeal papilloma
31, 32	Skin warts

EV = Epidermodysplasia verruciformis;
CIN = Cervical intraepithelial neoplasia;
VIN = Vulval intraepithelial neoplasia.

Attempts to treat laryngeal papillomata in humans with ionizing radiation were associated with malignant conversion.

Clinical effects

Skin warts

Skin warts (usually due to HPV 1–4) are benign and of little clinical consequence unless they become painful, in the case of plantar warts, or generalized as in certain immunocompromised individuals. The prevalence of warts in children aged 11–16 (the peak age) is about 10%. Transmission to others occurs by direct contact and regression of the lesions within a two year period is common. Treatment consists of cryosurgery, surgical removal or laser evaporation.

Oral papillomata

Oral papillomata occur in children and are caused by HPV type 2. Laryngeal papillomata (types 6 and 11) occur in infants born to mothers who have genital warts and there is a reported association between the presence of laryngeal papillomata and oro-genital sexual activity. These lesions are less likely to regress and usually require surgery.

Genital warts

Genital warts (condylomata acuminata) are usually sexually transmitted and are mainly caused by HPV-6, 11 and 16. The association of HPV infection with malignant conversion in both sexes is well established. In women, infection on the cervix, vulva and perianal regions predisposes to malignant change and 30% of women with vulval warts have cervical intraepithelial neoplasia. In the male, malignant conversion of penile warts has been described and HPV sequences (usually HPV-16) have been detected in nearly 50% of penile carcinomata.

The apparent increase in the incidence of cervical HPV infection over the past decade has coincided with a ten-fold increase in mortality from cervical cancer in women under the age of 35. There appears to be little doubt that a major factor in the aetiology of this tumour is the acquisition of HPV infection. As one would expect from DNA tumour virus models, although viral antigens are often present in premalignant lesions, they are absent from carcinoma tissue. However, HPV sequences are detected in over 90% of samples of cervical carcinoma tissue. It is important to note that, while the HPV genome exists in episomal form in benign warts and premalignant cervical lesions, it is integrated, or covalently bonded to chromosomal DNA in most malignant tissue.

Herpesviruses

Epstein–Barr virus (EBV) causes a lymphoma in marmosets and transforms lymphocytes into a state that enables them to be grown in continuous culture *in vitro*. The virus, originally isolated from Burkitt's lymphoma of African origin has been strongly associated with this tumour which is prevalent in certain localized areas of Africa. It is also associated with undifferentiated nasopharyngeal carcinoma, common in southern China, and with lymphomata occurring in the immunocompromised. The virus which causes the common disease infectious mononucleosis is, of course, ubiquitous and the localization of the tumours to certain geographic regions suggests that an additional factor, genetic or environmental, contributes to tumour formation. The removal of risk to individuals who move out of high prevalence regions promotes the view that a local environmental influence acts in conjunction with the virus. Immunosuppression due to malaria in Africa and drugs (or other immunosuppressive agents) in the immunocompromised, has been favoured by many as the most likely cofactor in Burkitt's lymphoma and related tumours. Cells in culture infected with EBV do not normally produce infectious virus but can be stimulated to do so. Studies of Burkitt's lymphoma tissue have revealed the presence of EBV DNA within the cell nuclei at a rate of 1–10 viral genome equivalents per cell. This viral DNA may be integrated into the cellular genome or exist in episomal form. Similar incorporation of EBV DNA has been found in cells from nasopharyngeal carcinoma. The continuous growth elicited by EBV in cultured lymphocytes may offer a clue to its role in human malignancies. In addition to this, chromosomal translocations known to occur in Burkitt's lymphoma cells may induce altered location and expression of cellular oncogenes, particularly c-myc. The oncogene is normally found on chromosome 8 and this chromosomal fragment is translocated in all B cell malignancies to chromosome 2, 14 or 22.

Herpes simplex virus type 2 can transform cells in culture, particularly if the lytic activity is prevented by ultra-violet light irradiation of the virus. The transformed cells have been transplanted into laboratory animals with resultant tumour formation and viral genomic sequences were present in the tumour cells. Epidemiological evidence indicated a strong correlation between herpes simplex type 2 infection of women and the development of cervical carcinoma (although not all studies confirmed this). Hybridization studies on tumour tissue have failed to reveal a significant level of integration of herpes simplex viral DNA within the cell nuclei. Thus HPV has replaced herpes simplex as the likely main viral cause of cervical cancer. The link with herpes simplex may indicate nothing more than the fact that herpes simplex type 2 and cervical cancer are both sexually transmitted conditions. Some favour the theory that herpes simplex is an important cofactor performing a triggering, or 'hit and run' role in tumour induction.

Retroviruses

The developments that led to the isolation and characterization of the first known human retrovirus have been mentioned in Chapter 16. The possible mechanism of oncogenicity of this virus (HTLV-1) was described earlier in this chapter. Isolation of this virus (reported in 1980) from a patient with cutaneous T cell leukaemia was followed by further isolations from similar patients and epidemiological studies confirmed the association of the presence of this virus with known areas of high incidence of the disease. The south-western part of Japan, Caribbean islands and southern states of the USA are regions in which the viral infection and the disease are prevalent and studies of expatriots from the West Indies revealed cases in London. A related virus discovered in a patient with a T cell variant of hairy cell leukaemia (HTLV-2) has not been confirmed as having an aetiological role in this (or any other condition) at the present time. HTLV-1 is a virus of low infectivity and is known to be transmitted by sexual contact, transfusion and materno-fetally in a similar way to HIV. The leukaemia develops several decades after infection and as with most oncogenic viruses, only a small minority of those infected develop the disease (approximately 1%). The associated cofactors are unknown, but the incidence of onset is higher in the summer and in those infected with microfilarial worms that tend to block lymphatic vessels.

Hepadnaviruses

Primary hepatocellular carcinoma (hepatoma) is a major cause of cancer mortality on a global scale although it is relatively uncommon in the Western world. It is highly prevalent in areas of high endemicity of hepatitis B and large prospective studies in Taiwan showed a clear association between the presence of virus persistence and tumour development. A closely related virus in woodchucks has been firmly associated with a carrier state and the development of liver cancer. However, the relatively low incidence of hepatoma in hepatitis B carriers in some regions has indicated the likelihood of environmental cofactors necessary for tumour formation. Levels of contamination of cereals, pulses and groundnuts with the liver toxin, aflatoxin, also correlate with the incidence of the tumour and there may be other cofactors (genetic and/or environmental).

Further reading

Rigby P. W. J. and Wilkie N. M. (1985) *Viruses and Cancer*. 37th Symp Soc Gen Microbiol. Cambridge University Press, Cambridge.

Singer A., Campion M. J. and McCance D. J. (1985) Human papillomavirus. *Br J Hosp Med*, **34**, 104–8.

Tooze J. (Ed) (1981) *DNA Tumour Viruses*. Cold Spring Harbor Laboratory, New York.

Weiss R., Teich N., Varmus H. and Coffin J. (1984) *RNA Tumour Viruses*. Cold Spring Harbor Laboratory, New York.

Index